STORIES FOR CHRISTMAS

STORIES

FOR CHRISTMAS

Edited by Mary Virginia Robinson

 JOHN KNOX PRESS
Richmond, Virginia

Library of Congress Catalog Card Number: 67-11202
© M. E. Bratcher 1967
Printed in the United States of America
J. 3667

To Mary Virginia Robinson—
whose careful and loving work enhances
the quality of each manuscript that she edits—
we, her friends and colleagues at John Knox Press,
have secretly dedicated this book.

Foreword

This anthology brings together a popular group of Christmas stories. The first of these, "The Man Who Owned the Stable," was published by John Knox Press in booklet form in 1943 and has gone through subsequent printings totaling more than 30,000 copies.

Other stories have followed, in a series welcomed by readers of every age. Seven are included in the present collection, along with five new ones.

The themes are varied. Some of the stories have a first-century setting in Palestine. Others show the spirit of Christmas influencing lives in modern situations. All offer enrichment for the Advent season.

Families will enjoy these stories as they look toward Christmas. In church and community libraries the collection will provide a valuable resource for program use. At any time, *Stories for Christmas* will make a treasured gift.

Contents

The Man Who Owned the Stable, *by Armand L. Currie* 11

The Boy Who Kept the Sheep, *by Kenneth G. Phifer* 19

The Empty Cup, *by Opal Menius* 29

The Pullers of the Star, *by Mary Lou Lacy* 43

The Littlest Shepherd, *by Dorothy D. Boulware* 51

A Star Is Born, *by Kenneth G. Phifer* 67

Incident in a Minor Province, *by Jack Abernathy* 75

Butter and Honey, *by Katharine Allyn See* 83

Mr. Jones Goes to Bethlehem, *by Harmon B. Ramsey* 89

Never in Jerusalem, *by Pauline Palmer Meek* 103

In Search of Christmas, *by James E. Fogartie* 113

My Son, *by Armand L. Currie* 121

The Man
Who Owned the Stable

by Armand L. Currie

Good morning! I am a stranger here . . . so strange that you may wonder at my presence. Perhaps you have never even thought of me. I am really not surprised, for as you celebrate this Christmas season, your mind is occupied by so many persons much more important than I that it would hardly be worth your while to level a single thought at me.

Nevertheless, I am human enough to have dreamed these many years of how it might feel to stand in the presence of people and relate to them the things I know about the birth of the Christ Child. That is why I am here. I have not come to claim a place for myself beside the shepherds of the field, and Mary and Joseph, and the Wise Men of the East. These persons should live alone and together in your heart. For fear that your graciousness might tempt you to lift me to their plane, I must forbid that you even know my name. It is enough for you to know that I am the man who owned the stable.

It seems strange that I should have been drawn into this, the most thrilling drama the world has ever known. It happened so unexpectedly. It was in the year that Caesar Augustus sent out his decree that all the world should be taxed and that every living being should report to his own city. I was a resident of Bethlehem. Right excited were we all when we learned that into our little town there would soon come thousands of visitors . . . men with their wives and children from far and near to pay homage and duty to the throne of Rome. Some of us were bewildered, for we knew that Bethlehem was ill prepared to shelter and feed the vast multitude that would descend upon us. We scarcely had opportunity to lay a single plan before the day came and our narrow streets were swarming with people. Many had come early that they might find a place to lay their heads. We, in our little home, were surprised to hear a tapping at the door.

"Sir," a stranger said, "we have come from afar; could you take us in? We are very weary, and have no place to go."

We were poor people and had not much to share. Yet, poor people are usually the ones who have the clearest understanding of a fellow man's need; and if perchance a poor man holds in his heart sympathy to match his understanding, he will not say nay to the needy at his door. It was but a little while before our humble home was filled.

As the day grew older and the crowd grew greater, I thought to wander through the streets and see all these strangers who had come. There they were, thousands of them. Families were trying to keep together. Men looked troubled. Women were sagging with fatigue. Children cried for food and sleep. It was a strange and thrilling day for Bethlehem.

To escape the push and confusion of the throng, I entered the nearby inn. Its candlelit lobby was quiet compared with the street outside. The flickering light danced across the faces of a score of persons who had been fortunate enough to find shelter there. A man and his wife and three small children sat close together. They seemed awed by the strangeness of their surroundings, and I thought that I could see in their faces a look of yearning for home. In the center of the lobby stood a circle of men. They had the swaggering air of experienced travelers. They had rubbed shoulders with the world before and had thus learned how to be at home away from home. Perhaps they had met in other places and were enjoying the renewal of old acquaintances. There were other inn dwellers, too. As they moved about and talked with one another, the very tone of their voices was enough to make one know that they did not like having to be in Bethlehem. They hated the Roman government. They resented being herded in to be taxed and counted like sheep. Their trouble, however, was hardly worth noticing.

Presently the door opened from without and a man with his beautiful young wife entered. For a moment they stood together and whispered; then she withdrew into the shadows while he walked through the room, evidently in search of the innkeeper.

"May I be of some service to you, sir?" It was the innkeeper himself.

"Why . . . why, yes," the stranger answered nervously. "Yes, you may . . . that is, I hope you may. You see, I am a stranger here. My name is Joseph. My wife and I have come from Nazareth and we have no place to stay."

"I am sorry, my good man, very sorry; the place is filled; we have no room."

"But perhaps you could give us just a corner," Joseph pleaded. "It is urgent. We must find a place . . ."

It was the wrong thing for Joseph to say. The keeper of the inn was far too prosperous that night to even consider being inconvenienced, especially by any such urgency. While Joseph still begged for a place to stay, the keeper was leading him toward the door as if to hurry him and his lovely wife along. Opening the door he bowed positively. "I am very sorry indeed, there is no corner left." . . . As the latch clicked, someone laughed.

No room . . . no shelter . . . no bed! I had read about such things happening to people. Now it was happening before my very eyes, in my own home town of Bethlehem. It was unbelievable.

Why I should have walked out into the night after the strangers I do not know; but I did, and there they stood, in the shadow of the shelter under which there was no room. I could see the woman's face. She was frightened, and clung to Joseph's arm. Joseph was frightened too, and dejected. I heard him say, "If I could only tell them what is about to happen and who is about to be born, then there would be room." But even as he spoke, Joseph knew that no one would understand. Mary knew too, for she whispered, "No, Joseph, no . . . it would be too much to ask one to believe, now."

Being an humble man and timid, I was never much for talking with strangers about their troubles. Perhaps if I had waited long enough for my head to conquer my heart I would have passed them by as if I neither knew nor cared about them in their plight. Yet, there was something about those two people that made me cast my shyness to the winds. I could not walk off whistling with those two faces before my eyes. I crept over a little closer, and as if the darkness were drawing the three of us together with strong arms I dared to say, "Could I help you, strangers?"

A glimmer of hope danced for a moment across Joseph's face. "We have no place to rest," he said. I tried to cheer them both with a smile that reflected a poor man's understanding, but there was not much to smile about. In that hour they needed not just understanding, but understanding that would go to work.

"I have no fine place to offer you, for I, too, am poor," said I; "yet bound so closely together by such a bond, it may be that the three of us can find a way. I own a stable. Perhaps I should not even mention it, for it was built for cattle. It is humble, and the door is very low. Still, it is mine; it is all I have. In it the straw is fresh and clean and sweet, and may be even soft, made so by the welcome of my heart to you."

Joseph looked at me, and then at Mary with a question in his eye. She answered with a tear that was lighted by a smile. "Would the Son of God mind being born in a stable? The son of man might, but not the Son of God! The stable would be as a palace for Him if it had in it the light of human love and the soft sweetness of human kindness."

The innkeeper would at least lend us a lantern. So with the lantern in my hand, I led the way to the stable. My heart was throbbing with kindness. Yet, I was glad that the night hid from my guests the expression of amusement that must have been in my face. The humble couple were looking forward with such eagerness to the coming of their child that they even made bold to think of him as the very Son of God. Well, such is life, I thought, with all its fantastic hopes and dreams. A million other parents had dreamed great dreams for their firstborn.

Reaching the stable, I hung the lantern by the door and bade my guests a good night. Walking home a strange happiness seemed to flood my heart. I wondered why. The whole incident was so absurd. I was entertaining guests in a stable! I had offered the shelter of a stable to two strangers, and they had gladly accepted it. For years to come the neighbors would laugh at my crude hospitality. Yet something seemed to tell me that I had done a grand thing. Nobody else had thought of offering his stable for a shelter, and what if the neighbors did laugh? Behind their laughter would be the realization that I had done the best I could with what I had. Even if my efforts were very humble, no one would deny that my motive was very high. That was it, that was why I felt so happy; I had done a decent thing! What on earth can bring greater happiness to any man than the sense of having done a decent thing?

At midnight there was a knock at my door. I was almost afraid to answer. It might be Joseph, I thought, come to tell me that he and his beautiful wife had talked things over and had decided not to stay in my stable. Their child deserved a better place to be born than in a stable. Of course, I could not blame them. Yet I hoped hard that they were not going away, for if they should leave, they would take something I was cherishing in my heart which I wanted badly to keep.

It was not Joseph at the door. It was a shepherd, wild with excitement. "What is it, neighbor?" I asked. "Have the wolves attacked your sheep?"

"No," he shouted fast, "as we guarded the flocks we were startled by the swish of an angel's wing, and he, seeing our fright, said, 'Be not afraid; I bring you good tidings of great joy. There is born unto you this day in the city of David a Saviour which is Christ, the Lord. And this shall be the sign . . . ye shall find Him in a stable.'"

"Shepherd," said I, "am I dreaming, or are you crazy?"

The shepherd was in no mood to quibble. "In a stable," he shouted back as he rushed away, "your stable."

There lay the babe in the manger. "Why, congratulations, Joseph," I said. "Is he not a fine boy, though? May he bring you many blessings."

"He shall," Joseph replied, "and may He bring you many blessings, kind friend, for this child is the Son of God."

"Now, Joseph, calm yourself. We all feel that way about our firstborn," I said. "And as for you, shepherd, and your angel story . . . well, strange things do happen, but I have always contended that the two persons who never fail to take the prize are a new father and a moon-struck shepherd. . . . Well, blessings on you, little child; may you ever honor your father's joy in you."

Then, later, there came three other men, strangers. They were not humble folk as we. Yet, they seemed not to care that the child whom they sought had been born in a stable. As if to explain their presence, one said, "We are searching for the King. We have seen His star. We have followed it here." As they knelt before the child, they opened gifts of gold, and frankincense, and myrrh, and worshiped Him. They had seen His star, the King's star! They had followed its light.

The King of kings, born in my stable! Could it be that this was heaven's blessing upon one who had shown crude but honest kindness to two strangers?

In the years that followed, my neighbors did not laugh as I had thought they might. They looked at me with a sort of pride. As the child grew and His fame soared high and wide, I could hear mothers whisper to their children as I passed them in the streets, "Look, child, there is the man who owned the stable." I was happy, of course; yet, I was embarrassed too. Christ had been born in my *stable*. I determined to make it up to Him somehow. I wanted Him to understand that if I had known who was about to be born that night, He would certainly have been given a more honorable place.

One day I dared to speak with one of His friends about my embarrassment. "John," said I, "the Saviour was born in my stable. It was a poor beginning for a King. I am an old man now, and I should like to die with the thought that I had done something better for Him than that."

"Others have done no better," he replied, "for even now He hath not where to lay His head. Yet for this He seems to have no care; only time after time His weary yearning is to have a place to rest, not in buildings made with hands but in human hearts, hearts that are decent and clean and kind."

"John," said I, "do you suppose He would deign to accept the shelter of my heart?"

John reckoned that He would. . . . And He did.

The Boy
Who Kept the Sheep

by Kenneth G. Phifer

The day was wearing thin in places, and here and there patches of darkness were showing through. The shepherds gathered a little closer to one another. There is a lonesomeness about the twilight time that is unlike that of any other period of the day. It gets down into the very soul and stretches out vast empty spaces in the heart. The men stood in silence for a while, the silence of those who are much alone and for whom simply the presence of another person is comradeship enough. The long slope of the hill was reaching down now into a deep pocket of the night, and Simon the eldest spoke: "Darkness comes racing through the valley. It is time to gather in the strays before night has rubbed all the gold from off the mountaintops." They stood still for a moment just as though no one had spoken; then Simon moved away into the shadows, and the others followed. Off they went, their staffs clicking harshly now and then upon a stone, their long strides making gentle rustling sounds in the grass.

Joseph followed Amos as closely as though he were his

shadow. It was not that he was afraid, but after all this was the first time he had ever been out in the hills in the twilight, and the long shafts of blackness that lay upon the ground were cold, unpleasant things. They moved at times like the fingers of some hidden giant reaching out for him. Joseph knew that he must not show any sign of fear. There had been many weeks of pleading before his brother had consented to this adventure, and he had done so then only after stern warnings about interference with the sheep, about too much talk, and above all about wandering off and getting lost in the darkness.

Amos was moving to his right now, slowly, carefully, stooping every now and then to peer into some clump of bushes, occasionally parting a thicket with his staff in case some lamb had wandered off from his mother and become entangled in the underbrush. Joseph stopped each time Amos did, and he stooped, too, to peer intently into some patch of blackness, looking for the spot of white that would indicate a sheep. Apparently all were safe, and at last Reuben appeared, coming from the opposite direction. "All are in this way," he said. Without further words the two men turned and walked back toward the crest of the hill, Joseph trailing along, his short legs moving quickly to keep abreast of the long strides of the others.

Someone had built a fire that cast a rosy gleam for a short distance into the surrounding gloom. The shepherds huddled close to the blaze, for the evening wind was brisk and cold. The stars were out here and there, but they were winter stars with a chill aloofness about them that made Joseph think wistfully of the friendly skies of summer when the stars hung low and whispered secrets to boys and girls. There was one star, it was true, that had come up across the sky these last few nights, its light softer and more brilliant than any of the rest. Joseph looked toward the horizon, searching for it eagerly as for an old friend, but to his disappointment he discovered that it was not there tonight. At least it was not there yet, and he sank back to rest against a rock. He had seen it from his room in his father's house in Bethlehem, had seen it and wondered at its beauty and had talked about it to Rachel, the innkeeper's little daughter. She had noticed it too, and they spent hours describing it to one another. Joseph had talked to his mother about the star, but she had not seen it and did not understand his questions. But then grown people were always blind to such matters. So the star had remained his and Rachel's secret and he wondered idly if she were looking for it now, too, and if she were disappointed that so far tonight it had not come.

The talk of the older men droned on monotonously into the night and Joseph's sense of excitement began to fade. For months he had begged for this opportunity, for this night of watching with the shepherds on the hillside while they kept their sheep. For months he had cajoled and pleaded, and finally Amos had said, quite surlily and not in friendly fashion at all, that he might come. Now that he was here, he was beginning to feel that it was not the adventure of which he had dreamed. Once a lion roared in the distance, but no animal had come close to them, much less tried to attack the sheep. No robbers had been reported in the vicinity for weeks now, and there seemed little danger from that direction, tonight at least. The hours were beginning to drag. The ground was cold and hard and his cloak but little protection from the dampness and the wind. And the shepherds? Well, it seemed that they were content simply to sit and talk between long silences. Occasionally one would raise his head and peer off into the darkness in the direction of some movement among the sheep. But for the most part, Joseph concluded to himself, both the shepherds and their talk were rather dull. His head began to nod, and invisible strings tugged at his eyelids as though trying to pull them shut and tie them tight in sleep. Then suddenly through half-opened eyes he saw his star. While he had drowsed it had moved across the heavens right above their heads. Still it moved, and still it glowed like no star he had ever seen before. Excitedly he pulled at Amos' robe.

"The star," he cried, "there it is—my star. Do you not see it, my brother?"

Amos grumpily turned his head and followed with his eyes the lad's pointing finger. He gazed intently at the heavens for a long, long time.

"Yes," he said at last, "I think I see it. It does shine brighter than the rest."

The grumpiness had all gone out of his voice and his tone manifested actual interest. For a time they sat apart from the others and watched the star, the man and the boy—sat silently, bound together by the invisible bond of a vision shared. They sat and said no word to their friends, who, apparently noticing nothing strange, continued their idle talk.

The odd appearance of movement that the star had shown had ceased. It seemed now to hang very low and very still over Bethlehem itself. Joseph suddenly realized, with a little twinge of envy, that it looked as though it hung directly over the part of town where Rachel lived. Surely she must be awake and watching and aware that their star was closer to her than it was to him. She might see things about it that he had not noticed. All the anticipation that he had felt in planning to tell her on the morrow of the night spent with the shepherds began to fade away. The distant roar of the lion, the tales of robbers that the men had told, the wind of the desert that knifed through one's clothes to cut into the very skin—all of these dimmed in importance in the light of the star so very close to where he knew Rachel must be watching.

Then it happened—suddenly, like the bursting splendor of the sun over Mount Lebanon at dawn, only far more splendid, a thousand times more glorious. It was the star that seemed to shatter into a million fragments of white, sparkling beauty, seemed to shatter as though its glory were beyond its containing any longer. The silver slivers spread across the sky toward the very hill on which he sat. As they spread they became like wings, like angel wings, and suddenly the sky was filled with a whole multitude of heavenly hosts. Their voices swelled on the breeze in the glorious harmony of a song that was the most beautiful melody Joseph had ever heard. It had within it the bubbling lilt of laughter and strong notes of triumph as though in celebration of a great victory. Through it all, too, there was a deeper undertone that reminded one of an ache in the human heart. At first there were no words, only the melody on the wind. Then the voices swelled and the hearers were able to distinguish words in their own tongue, "Glory to God in the highest, and on earth peace, good will toward men."

Joseph's heart stood still. He sprang to his feet, then quickly fell back to his knees, knowing instinctively that no one must stand in the presence of such glory. He could see that Amos and the others had beheld the spectacle and that they, too, had fallen to their knees and covered their faces.

The night was filled with the voices, and still they came and still they sang, "Glory to God in the highest." For an endless eternity they came, and the magic fell like a multicolored mantle over the hill. Even the flocks were still, and the gentle moaning of the wind from off the desert died away in the great chorus of the angels. Then like the silken note of a harp against the background of many voices came one voice saying, "Fear not: for, behold, I bring you good tidings of great joy, which shall be to all people. For unto you is born this day in the city of David a Saviour, which is Christ the Lord. And this shall be a sign unto you; Ye shall find the babe wrapped in swaddling clothes, lying in a manger." The voice was gone and the chorus swelled once more, "Glory to God in the highest."

Not one of them knew whether it was for a moment or for an hour that they waited tense and taut, listening to the thing that had come bursting from the star. At such times it does not matter whether it is a moment or an hour. Time is irrelevant when the angels sing.

At last the light began to fade and the voices were but thin golden whispers on the wind, whispers so soft that the sudden thought seized Joseph that perhaps he had imagined the whole marvelous scene. Yet there was Amos with his bowed head and there were Reuben and Simon and all the others, and there was the silence that filled the air with richer speech than any tongue might utter. No one and no thing moved. The trees and the grass and the animals were like the men, gripped by the deep quiet and the dark night. It was as though a mighty hand had suddenly torn aside the curtain of mystery that separates men from eternity, showing them one glimpse of what lies beyond, then pulling the curtain quickly back into place lest the sight of such holy things shatter their brains into fragments of madness.

Amos was the first to speak. "It is a sign," he said quietly, as though not to disturb any last lingering note of angel voices that might still lurk behind the silence; "we must go. Let us now go even unto Bethlehem, and see this thing which is come to pass, which the Lord hath made known unto us."

No one else spoke a word, but each man gathered his cloak about his shoulders and clutched his staff firmly. It was old Simon who first realized what they were about to do.

"The sheep," he said. "There is no one to watch the sheep. We cannot leave them to wander off into the darkness. Some one of us must stay."

They all looked at one another, each almost defiantly declaring with his eyes that it would not be he who would stay behind. Then someone looked at Joseph. Oh, he had been afraid of that. He tried to slip behind his brother and hide in the shadow of his garment, but it was Amos himself who turned full upon him and voiced the unspoken thought of all.

"You are the youngest, Joseph," he said gently, half hoping that the lad would offer to stay and be pleased at the responsibility that was placed upon him and the confidence that would be shown. But the boy said nothing. He could not, for the lump that filled his throat was his heart. He feared lest any attempt at speech would release a torrent of tears.

"Stay, lad," said Amos, "and when we return we will tell you all the things we see and then you, too, may go and bear your gift to the King."

Still Joseph said nothing. He stood rooted to the spot, dumb and speechless, his heart sinking beneath the weight of his disappointment, feeling nothing but a great hurt inside. They took his silence for consent and moved off into the night. The boy watched the moving whiteness of their garments as far as he could see them. He fought back the tears, and turned finally toward the sheep. He had a job to do, and since he had to stay he would do it. For the next few minutes he moved about the flocks, speaking softly to the restless, driving a lamb back here and there that threatened to stray too far from its mother. His head was still filled with the memory of the angels and the song. He found that if he closed his eyes he could live it all over again just as though it were happening for the first time and they were there before him. When at last the sheep were still again he sat down and leaned his head back against a rock. He shut his eyes very tightly now and saw once more the star and its sudden glory and then the chorus of heavenly messengers. He could even believe that he heard the harmony once more. In the re-living of the magic moment he almost forgot his hurt and pain. A great brooding silence seemed to hang over the flocks now, and the night was a vast eternity of quietness.

Joseph nodded again, and those invisible strings were tugging at his eyelids. It was then that he saw him, a very little angel out of the chorus who, Joseph remembered, had stood to one side during the singing. He had noticed him because he was such a little angel, much smaller than himself. The little angel moved a step closer to the rock where Joseph sat, and to the boy's amazement he began to speak.

"I know how you feel. I was left, too—to watch over you while you keep the sheep. The rest of the angels fill the skies over a stable in Bethlehem where He lies, the King. And I am here, just like you. But see, it is right and proper that if anyone must stay behind to keep the sheep it should be we. For children are wiser than grown folk. Grown people need to see and touch and feel a thing before they will believe that it is true. Children know things in their hearts, see things with an inner eye. Your brother and his friends could not see the star, but you saw it when it first came up the sky. You and Rachel have watched it now for many nights. Your brother and his friends would not have believed the stories of the King unless they had gone to see Him with their eyes, and to touch His tiny fingers with their big rough hands, and to hear Joseph and Mary tell the wonder of it over and over. But you know that He is there because I tell you so—a little bit of a babe lying in a manger who is God's gift to men and women and especially to little children everywhere. Because you are a child you know the wonder and the mystery that cannot be seen or touched or talked about. You know that I am here but they do not, and they will not believe you if you tell them. That is why when the King proclaims, 'Blessed are little children, for theirs is the kingdom of heaven,' men will wonder and argue and write learned treatises upon His words and, except for a very few, will never know what He meant. Yes, and for long, long centuries to come, men will celebrate His birth and make spiritual pilgrimages to Bethlehem, and date all history from this hour. They will argue about Him and interpret His meaning so profoundly that no one can understand. For only children and the childlike will ever really know that meaning. Only they can come with wide-eyed wonder and with open hearts, and so only they can truly celebrate the birthday of the King. Only they, because they have no theories but receptive hearts." The very little angel sighed; it had been a long speech for him. "Yes," he said, "grown-up people are a problem. Blessed are little children, for of such is the kingdom of heaven."

Then he was gone. Or had he ever been there? Joseph was not sure. He only knew that the hurt inside was gone. Yes, it was right and proper that Amos and the others should have gone to see the wonders of which the angels sang. It was right and proper that he should stay behind. He could see it all in his heart, a little baby wrapped in swaddling clothes lying in a manger, the shepherds leaning over the strange scene in awe. Perhaps Rachel was in the background with her great wide eyes. Perhaps she would even touch the baby's hand, lay her finger reverently on His tiny palm. But not everyone could go running off to Bethlehem. Someone must watch the flocks.

The sun was high in the heavens when the men returned, talking excitedly among themselves of the strange and wonderful night. The sheep were scattered out over the hillside cropping the sparse grass contentedly. The boy was sound asleep against his rock. Amos prodded him awake with his staff.

"We have seen the King!" he cried. "Come, boy, choose a lamb and take it to the stable behind old Benjamin's inn. On your way, that you, too, may look upon Him with your eyes."

Joseph said nothing as he rose to his feet, but thought within himself, "I have seen the King. I have looked upon Him in my heart."

The boy who kept the sheep could not know that some day the King was to say, "Blessed are they that have not seen, and yet have believed." The boy who kept the sheep could not know that in the centuries yet to come the King would be born again and again in the magic of Christmas time, born again and again for all children and for all the childlike, and they would see Him, not with their eyes, but in their hearts.

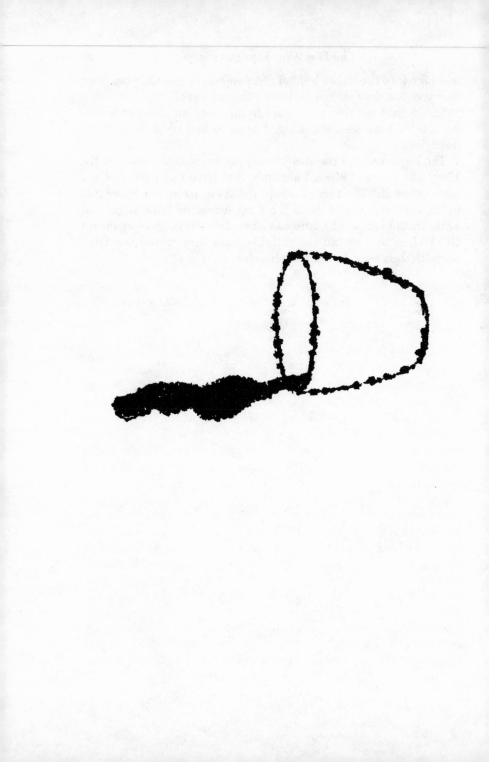

The Empty Cup

by Opal Menius

Never did any man love a woman as I loved my dark-eyed Rachel. When I wooed her, the light winds of spring were gently stirring the olive leaves in the garden of her father where her little sisters played. When I won her, the quiet evening star shone clear from the deep velvet of a summer sky. We were, that night, two shadows in a garden of shadows, but the gloom was only beauty to us in that time when no shadows lay across our lives. Rachel's laugh was as clear as the song of birds, and I prayed that it would ever ring as joyous and as sweet.

It was in October, in the time of the Feast of Booths, that I talked with her father. In that week spent by the Jews in remembering and in giving thanks for the joys of home and fireside, I spoke to him of the home I had made ready for Rachel. It was built of finest cedar, and my vine and fig tree flourished, though they were yet young and small. The old man's eyes were sad when he thought of the long, long journey from his house down to mine. But he was not blind to the unveiled joy in his daughter's eyes when she looked upon me, and her happiness was dear to his heart.

Soon we were no longer man and maiden, but bridegroom

and bride. Then, the week of feasting over, we began the journey to our home.

We traveled slowly down the winding and dusty road, stopping often to let the donkeys rest, or for no other reason than that we wished to explore some tempting hillside and valley. We would romp and race across the grassy meadows. She could run like the wind, but I, too, was fleet of foot. Sometimes, when I had finally caught her in my arms and stilled her laughter with a kiss, I would whisper the words of the good King David, "My cup runneth over."

Who would have thought that even greater joy was yet to be mine? We came, one day, to the end of our journey, and Rachel became the mistress of my home. She was like that proverbial woman made famous by our great King Solomon, she looked well to her household. My house of cedar was always clean. My table was loaded with the best of food. My own grapes quenched our thirst. My wife made sure that this was so; and she provided kisses and laughter and love as freely as she provided food.

Our neighbor, the good mother Hannah, used to say to me, "It is a noble woman you have taken to wife, my son. Her price is far above rubies." Hannah loved my Rachel and spent many happy hours with her. Hannah had borne sons and daughters, but they had in the fullness of time gone forth into homes of their own. Now Hannah had lonely hours to fill, and Rachel was the sunshine of her days.

I thought I knew all there was to know of joy. Then came October and the Feast of Booths again. This time, we had a new blessing for which to give thanks. Our newborn child lay in the fine fir-wood cradle I had so carefully made for him in the long months of waiting for his coming. There had been a day when, for the first time, Rachel's laughter was stilled, for she went down into the very valley of the shadow of death; and the child was precious to us not only because he was the firstborn but also because we knew that Rachel would never have another.

As the days went by, the joy of motherhood brought swift healing to my lovely wife, and soon the house rang with her happy laughter day and night. The child was gentle and sweet like his mother, but strong as a young fir tree. There never was a finer baby! My work at the carpenter shop suffered in those days, for I would suddenly find myself leaving a yoke for oxen half done while I fashioned a toy for the baby. When he waved his tiny fists in the air and crowed for joy over some simple gift of mine, and when his mother's smiling eyes met mine across his little cradle, I knew no happier man had ever lived.

Another October, with its Feast of Booths, came round, and we slept beneath the stars in the shelter I had prepared for my wife and my son, and we gave thanks from grateful, reverent hearts. I think it was during that week that I spoke to my wife of my plan to go over into Lebanon and buy cedar for some new building soon to begin. She was disturbed at the thought of the months we would be separated, but she saw it was needful that I should go. She agreed that, with old Hannah to be with them at night, she and the boy could manage at home.

I left them in Hannah's care. Only business of greatest importance would have taken me away from them. Though there were many strange and wonderful things to see on the journey, I lived only for the day of return. My thoughts were ever with my loved ones. Often I dreamed of the hour when I should reach home. For my son I had carved a toy lamb from the finest wood in Lebanon. Sometimes, in my dreams, he ran to meet me as I turned in at the gate. I would hold the lamb high above his head and he would reach for it and laugh. Sometimes, in my dreams, I would come home at evening and the child would be asleep in his fir-wood crib. I would gently place the lamb in his arms, and he would smile in his sleep. But how he would crow with joy when he awakened!

Actually, I came home at noontide. I thought the boy might be playing in the garden, and my wife sewing under the fig tree while she watched him. But there was no one in the garden.

"They are at the noonday meal in the house, then, or perhaps the child is having his afternoon rest," I thought. "The house is very quiet."

I tiptoed into my home quite softly. Yes, there he lay in his crib—the darling. How still he was and how beautiful he looked, lying there so quietly! How white his little face appeared! I had forgotten he was so pale. Rachel must have him in the sun more when the days are warmer, I thought.

Softly, I tiptoed to the crib. Gently I placed the lamb in his arms. This was just as I had dreamed it many, many times.

Why, then, did I feel an unrest? Whence this vague knowledge that all was not well?

His little arm had seemed cold. I touched it again. It was very cold—as cold as death. Snatching the blanket from over the child I gazed with horror at a deep red gash across his heart.

How long I stood there I do not know. I could not tear my tormented eyes from the body of my son. Neither could I understand. Clearly this could have been no accident. Why had anyone wished to murder a child as innocent as the lamb in his arms?

I raised my eyes at last and Hannah was standing in the doorway, tears running down her cheeks.

I said, "Who?"

She answered, "The soldiers."

I said, "Why?"

She answered, "By order of the king."

I said, "Rachel?"

She shook her head sadly and looked at me with sorrowful eyes as she stood aside from the doorway, allowing me to pass into the bedroom where my young wife was lying. Rachel lay so quietly that at first I thought she, too, was dead. I fell upon my knees beside her, but she did not seem to know that I was there. I poured out my sorrow and my love, but she seemed not to hear. My sorrow gave place to wrath, and I stormed against the slayer of my son with wild and bitter words, speaking with more feeling than knowledge, for, in my haste to reach home, I had not stopped to talk with people by the way, and so had not learned of the king's decree that all boy babies should be killed.

"There is nothing I—or any of us—can do," he wrote. "Come and take her if you want her. If you do not want her now, I shall understand. It may be better for you to dwell alone than with this child of sorrow. She will ever be welcome here. Leave her with us if it be your will."

Life for me had been no happier without Rachel. Besides, she was my wife. Sadly I returned to get her and bring her home. There was pity in her father's eyes, and in her mother's, as they made her ready and sent us on our way.

We set forth at sunrise and rode until night brought an end to safe journeying. In all that time, Rachel said no word of any kind. I talked of all the things I knew. She did not even seem to hear. We camped for the night. Perhaps Rachel slept. I do not know. I only know that it was well after midnight when I fell at last into an exhausted sleep.

We rose at dawn and began the second day's journey. With the coolness of the morning air, fresh courage rose within me and I began anew my attack on Rachel's indifference.

"Look at those lambs on the hillside," I exclaimed with enthusiasm. "The little black one runs around butting all the others. Is he not a frisky fellow?"

She gazed at the lamb without interest, then turned her eyes back to the winding road. I tried again.

"Those olive trees are growing very old. The owner should be replacing them soon. I have planted a new olive tree on the right side of our doorway. It is just a little tree, but already the sparrows have found it and are making a nest. The tree is so small it seems scarce able to bear the weight of the straw, but it stands up proudly as though it were glad to be the foundation of a home."

As I had expected, this was of no concern to Rachel. I rode on in silence.

Sometimes we met or passed other travelers on the road. I tried to interest Rachel in some of them.

"Look at that young bridegroom with his bride," I said once. "The bride must be twice as old as he. Will they be happy, do you think?" When Rachel did not answer, I continued, "If he

The Empty Cup

Nothing that I said seemed to arouse any feeling in
She lay quietly, gazing out of the window with dreamy ey

I thought, "This is grief and shock. She will recove
days go by. Time heals all things."

Was I the one person on earth whom time completel
or were there others who trusted and were disappoin
chel did not grow better. She never wept, and she alm
spoke. She went about her household work dutifully b
out interest. She would not be concerned with anyth
ever-changing beauty of the earth, the strange and u
able ways of the men and women who were our neigh
little words and gifts of love I brought her, all were a
unnoticed.

As though in a fog she wandered through the days an
and every day she grew thinner. There was a clouded
her eyes, and a hollowness in her voice that reminded r
Bathsheba. Old Bathsheba had a devil, and wander
through the hills around Nazareth, howling and shriekir
one came near her. I would rather have seen Rachel d
to see her become a second Bathsheba.

A year went by, and then another year. Month
month, each filled with slow and hopeless days.

I said, "I will send Rachel back to her father
Beneath the roof where she once was so happy she
happiness again. Wrapped in the warm protection of
ents' love, she may find peace. In the sunlit garden
lighthearted young sisters, she may learn to laugh again."

So I took her back to her father's house, over the r
were filled with memories of a happier time. I left her
parents and returned alone to my home, trying in vain
the shock and concern in the eyes of her loved ones v
beheld her.

I filled the lonely months of waiting with eager dre
healed and happy Rachel returning to be once more
and joy of my house. Six months had passed when
came from her father which ended all my hopes.

chases her over these hillsides, he will not have so much difficulty catching her as I once had catching you. Remember?"

Apparently she did not remember.

Suddenly, I saw a gruesome thing. A leper woman stood near the roadside, begging. She dared not come too near, but, from the distance at which the law held her, she begged for food for herself and her son. The woman was ragged and disheveled. Her clothes were exceedingly dirty, but since her fingers had already been eaten away by the disease, she could scarcely have been blamed for that. Her matted, dirty hair hung down over a face fearfully marked by disease. Even a casual observer would know that she had few days remaining in this world.

In marked contrast to the aged, filthy, diseased woman, the boy stood fresh and young and fair. He was a little fellow, not more than five years old. When, with pleading tones, the woman begged food for herself and the child, the boy ran down to the roadside and brought back whatever compassionate wayfarers saw fit to toss him. I perceived that, in spite of all her protests, the lad placed the tastiest morsels between the lips of his mother.

In happier days I would have done all I could to spare Rachel such a sight as this. Now, I thought that the sorrows of others, in this case far greater than hers, might serve to take her mind away from her own troubles.

"Poor little boy," I said. "What will become of him when his mother dies? She surely cannot live much longer."

But the sorrows of others touched Rachel no more than their joys.

The roads were crowded with travelers at this time of year. Toward noon, two men large and coarse in appearance rode up behind us. The road was narrow at this place. We rode between a steep cliff on the right and a sharp drop into a valley on the left. Passing was clearly impossible, and the men were annoyed at the slowness of our going. I urged my donkey to greater speed, but either the situation had made no impression upon Rachel's clouded mind, or else it made no difference to her. She continued her slow, unheeding pace. The men grumbled, then they grew mocking.

"Look you, Jacob," said the smaller one. "It is a pair of snails that have climbed out of the hillside and choose to make a little journey into town."

"I am thinking, Simon," answered Jacob, "that the town will be as dead as Sodom and Gomorrah long ere they arrive."

Simon's laugh was long and loud. Encouraged by the appreciation of his friend and, no doubt, by the wine of which he must have partaken long and heartily, he drew forth his sword.

"A probe from this good blade might bring forth speed from even a snail," he grinned, as he prodded my wife firmly in the back.

Wild anger rushed through me. I had no sword, but I seized a bag of provisions from the back of my donkey and swung it at Simon fiercely. He dodged it, and in so doing rammed his donkey against the one my wife was riding, causing its hind feet to slip backward over the cliff.

For a second we stared breathlessly at the struggling animal. My wife held firmly to her mount, but the expression of her face did not change. Even when the panting little donkey succeeded in getting his four feet firmly planted once more upon the path, she gave no indication of any relief she may have felt. Weak as I was with fear, I still had the strength to marvel that any human being could be so indifferent to her own life or death.

Then Jacob was charging at me with drawn sword. Even as I leaped from my donkey and dodged the blow, I glanced at Rachel. Looking into her eyes I saw—and this was the thing that finally broke my heart—that she was as indifferent to my danger as she had been to her own. Her calm, uncaring expression had not changed.

There was no heart left in me for fighting. Truly, Jacob could have slain me there and I would not have opposed him. But his companion had become alarmed at the seriousness of the quarrel and had caught Jacob's arm. With some difficulty he succeeded in restraining Jacob, and, as soon as the path had widened, hurried him along his way. My wife and I rode on in silence.

Toward sunset we came to a little spring by the roadside. The water trickled down from a rock to make a crystal pool at its base. Green grass, generously sprinkled with flowers, grew around the clearing. Several tall trees added beauty and peace to the scene. The sheer loveliness of the place startled me out of the dark brooding into which I had fallen. I glanced at Rachel, but her troubled eyes still rested on the road ahead.

"We might as well eat here," I said. "Truly, it seems a place good for rest and refreshment."

Apparently we were not the only ones who thought so. A man and his wife and their small son were also camping by the spring and were preparing for their evening meal. They seemed a friendly family of simple folk. Feeling the need of human companionship after the long and difficult journey, I went over to them and we began to talk. The child played quietly, dipping his tiny fingers into the spring and letting the water trickle off.

I learned that the strangers were on their way to Nazareth, and that the man, like me, was a carpenter. Soon we were deep in a discussion of the best way to fashion a yoke that would not hurt the neck of the animal that wore it. The woman spoke pleasantly to my wife, who was listlessly setting out our supper. When Rachel returned no answer I explained that my wife was not well. The woman's eyes were gentle and sympathetic.

As she sliced a loaf of good homemade brown bread the woman talked to me. They had been living in Egypt, she said, but now they were going home.

"You have a lovely little son," I said. In truth the boy was fairer than the lily of the valley. I could not seem to take my eyes from him. Somehow, watching the boy, I felt completely quiet and at peace—a feeling strange to me.

"Thank you," the woman said. She smiled. "He seems to make friends wherever he goes. Sharon, the woman in whose home we found lodging in Egypt, loved him very much. She was quite ill when we first came to live with her. Day by day, as she cared for the child in the garden while I was busy, she seemed to grow better. Sometimes I wonder if the sunshine and fresh air were what she had been needing."

"Perhaps it was the renewed interest in life a child can bring," I said, for Rachel was out of hearing.

The mother continued her story. "Sharon's heart was heavy when she knew that we would not be in Egypt today, for this is the child's birthday. She prepared for the lad a bottle of fresh juice from the grapes of her vine. That vine is the pride of her life. It is a special one, crossbred in a way that only she knows, and it produces grapes of an especially rare and delicate flavor. She is famed throughout all the region for the luscious fruit. She insisted on giving me this bottle of juice for the boy, and on baking him a little cake of honey and dates, so that he may celebrate his birthday even though we are neither in Egypt nor at home. The child has talked eagerly of the good things all day long. He loved Sharon, and I think the food and drink will taste even better because they came from her."

"I think they should taste quite good, no matter whence they came," I said, eyeing the rich red liquid the mother was pouring into a cup.

The little boy had run up eagerly and was watching with bright-eyed anticipation. With the utmost caution, he took the cup carefully in one hand and the golden brown honey cake in the other. He walked over toward the little spring where a few smooth stones made a suitable place for a small boy to sit down.

The clattering of hoofs diverted my attention to the road. Another party was stopping by the spring. I gave a groan, for it was Jacob and his friend Simon. They seemed not to notice me. The donkeys leaped thirstily for the water, sending up a cloud of dust that almost choked us.

"Ah, water!" shouted Jacob, jumping from his donkey with haste. "Not so good as wine, perhaps, but truly my thirst is great. Out of my way, child."

He gave the little boy a shove that sent him sprawling into the dust. The precious honey cake flew in one direction, the cup in the other; and the rich red liquid spilled out and soaked like blood into the ground.

I watched the little boy get slowly to his feet. I waited for his howl of anger and frustration. There was only Jacob's boisterous laughter, followed by a great stillness. Not one of us moved, but Jacob's eyes turned uncertainly toward the father of the child who stood in the shadows not far away.

The child's soft voice broke the stillness. "Gone," he said, looking down at his empty cup. The word was not a reproach. He seemed, rather, to be trying to convince himself that this thing had really happened to him.

"Gone it is, and gone I must be," shouted Jacob, with another worried glance at the child's father, who had stepped forward from the shadows. Jacob hastily mounted his donkey and rode away, closely followed by Simon.

"Gone," the baby said again, this time with complete and full realization. He picked up his empty cup, washed it carefully in the spring, filled it to the brim with the clear cold water and drank long and deeply. I could not believe the depths of quietness in his eyes. I looked in vain for anger, frustration, bitterness—there was only infinite calm. Quietly, he took bread from the plate his mother had prepared. Sitting down upon the rock he began to eat and drink.

A gasp at my side made me turn. Rachel was looking at the boy and there were tears on her cheek. Then, over the rim of the cup, the child's clear eyes met hers, and a look passed between them that was not for me to understand.

From somewhere far off, a night bird called. The bright evening star appeared from behind a cloud. A feeling of peace came upon me so deep that I no longer struggled even to think. The rest of that evening I remember only dimly, as though it were a dream. I think that we ate our food. I know that later the child and his mother and father departed, for they said an extra hour of travel this day would make it possible for them to reach Nazareth on the morrow. Rachel and I spread out our blankets. I drew mine over me tightly and sank instantly into deep and dreamless sleep.

It was very early morning when I awakened. Sitting up and rubbing sleep-filled eyes, I perceived that the red sun was only beginning to rise beyond the hill. Then I saw that Rachel was not under the blanket beside me.

I looked toward the spring; but she was not there washing her face in the cool water, as I had hoped she might be. I looked across the clearing to the woods beyond, but she was nowhere to be seen. Panic seized me. Had her weary mind at last given way and was she wandering like old Bathsheba across the hills? Or had the little boy, the one being on earth with the power to attract her, so bewitched her that she had left all else to follow him?

I looked up the road in the direction from which we had come. I leaped to my feet, my heart beating wildly. For, lo, Rachel was coming! And a great joy filled my heart—for she sat upon the saddle tall and straight, riding like a queen. There was a smile upon her lips, and her eyes, clear and shining, met mine with the old look of loyalty and love.

And before her on the saddle, his curly head just reaching her heart, the leper's child came riding.

The Pullers of the Star

by Mary Lou Lacy

Once upon another time, not so long ago, but perhaps last year or even the one before, there was in Paradise a most select small group of little girl angels, who were known throughout Heaven as the Christmas Cherubs. They were given this name simply because on a Christmas morning, Saint Peter had heard a gentle tap at his gate and had opened it to find four little girls seeking admittance to the Glorious Kingdom of God. They had not come there together, nor had they been acquainted in their sojourn on the faintly remembered Earth. They had merely been transported with one accord and that most uniquely on the Day of All Days—the Birthday of the Blessed Infant.

The kindly Keeper-of-the-Gate picked up his pen to enter their names in the Great Book. "Who's first?" he said, as gently as he knew how, for the tiny figures seemed almost too tiny to be able to speak. He watched them turn and gaze from side to side. And then he knew that, until that moment, each little angel had felt herself to be alone. Then one reached out her hand to find the solace of another being, and she in turn reached too, until all four found courage in each other and one found the words to speak.

"Oh, sir, does it have to be one of us—one of us at a time? Can't it be all four?"

This was an unheard-of thing within the Pearly Gates. But Saint Peter smiled his kindest, most understanding smile and said, "Why, sure, we'll take you all together." And because he knew no other name to write, he put in his Book of Life, "The Christmas Cherubs"—and still holding hands, they entered into the Holy City of the King.

From that time on, henceforth and forevermore, the four little girl angels were always together. 'Tis true, they very shortly overcame their timidity and often chattered so loudly that even Saint Peter wondered how he ever thought them without voice. 'Tis true, they very soon overcame their feeling of strangeness, for there was no spot in the Celestial City that they had not explored and made their playground. But 'tis also true that the Christmas Cherubs were never, never separated. They had their little differences, you may be sure. They sometimes came close to tears when one little cherub was pursued by her dreadful earthly habit of teasing and let it get the best of her. On such an occasion, the cherubs were practicing Christmas music, hoping ever so hard to sing true enough to join the Heavenly Chorus. They were just finishing up the last part of "Away in a Manger," when someone's voice was not exactly on the very note that it should have been.

The First Little Angel spoke: " 'Tis such a shame that someone has to ruin it all. Someone's voice is out of tune."

Then the Second Little Angel said: "It was not I who squeaked at the last."

And the Third: "Neither did I. I sang it right."

And the Fourth: "Do not look at me, for I can sing as well as any."

Then the First again: "The way to tell for certain is to sing again, and each alone. I'll be first." And she sang again to her own satisfaction.

"That's good!" said the Second Little Angel. "Now I'll prove my voice." And she, too, was without embarrassment.

Then the Third Little Angel took her turn and said, "That sounded fine to me."

But, alas, the Fourth did sing alone and 'twas quite true, she was the guilty one.

And the First Little Angel began to sing off key, and three little angels laughed while one little angel cried. But the three were soon to be ashamed and they put their wings around the Fourth Little Angel and loved her up close and said, "Just you keep practicing, Honey Angel, and you'll sound perfect—better than the rest of us."

They really had no true disagreements, just a few natural, minor differences, such as one pair of wings growing more rapidly than the rest, but the owner hastened to see her mistake in bragging, and hurriedly added that she was probably the oldest of the four when they left the earth, and her wings should develop first. Oh, they were truly friends—these loving little cherubs.

Now the time of year was approaching when assignments to duty would be made by the Chairman of Worth-While Projects, and all the angels in the Holy City were speculating as to the part each one would play in the most special time of all, the Birthday of the Babe. The Heavenly Education Committee called a meeting for the purpose of explaining the system of merit to all new inhabitants of the Holy City, and you may be sure that the four Christmas Cherubs elbowed their way through the Celestial Citizens until they found themselves on the very front row.

They planned not to miss one single word that would explain more fully the great participation to come. For was this not their first Christmas in the Heavenly Kingdom, and were they not still children to whom Christmas is the Day of Days? And had they not heard that the way in which duties were performed decided most definitely which angels would be given which Joyous Jobs at this special time? They had discussed it often among themselves and had, with one accord, decided that to be the Pullers of the Christmas Star would be the greatest of the Joyous Jobs. The star that led the Wise Men long ago must still send forth its light, so that men, even now, might be able to follow and worship. What a magnificent part of Christmas—this pulling of the Star! How they would work to deserve such an appointment!

The Chairman of Worth-While Projects cleared his throat and began his explanation. He spoke in words that were simple so that everyone, even the Christmas Cherubs, could have no doubt as to the purport of his message. And when he finished, the newcomers clearly understood that the part each Celestial Being played in celebrating the Birthday was deserved, was earned, was given him because of the job that Being had done in preparing the heart of a Human for the special time ahead. Now you and I have always heard of the Christmas Angel. Maybe a few of us have seemed to feel the mystical presence on rare occasions, but we have never truly believed that one really hovered near. How greatly wrong we've been! For here were the Christmas Cherubs being assigned a soul over which to hover and told that their angelic participation in the heavenly celebration to come was dependent on the amount of good their hovering did. The cherubs, because of their inexperience and age, were given only one mortal to observe, to endeavor to influence, to make more worthy of celebrating the Birthday of our Lord.

Immediately following the motion for adjournment, the four inseparables withdrew to their own private, special spot in the Celestial Kingdom, and set out to form their plan.

"We know nothing about this human being we have been assigned," said the First.

"No," said the Second, "and I should think that finding her out would be our first step."

Then the Third reminded, "We do know that the human is a Woman, and in my opinion, that makes it hard to start with."

But the Fourth had an idea. "I think we should go down and watch," she said, "then return to decide where we should begin."

The First agreed, and said, "Then let's not waste time. Let's go and hover over her, and see what's to be done."

But the Second said, "I'm not sure I know just how to hover. I've never done it before."

Then the Third took her hand and comforted her, saying, "From the Angels of Long Standing I sought the answer to that very problem. Come on, Honey Angel, I'll show you how to hover."

Then spoke the Fourth Little Angel, "You'll have to show me, too, 'cause I'm no good at it yet."

And so the Christmas Cherubs made their first return flight to earth, and for one solid week they hovered and hovered over their Problem Person. They watched her make her Christmas List and shuddered at its lack of meaning. They peeked into her pocketbook and trembled as she proportioned for herself and the needy. They learned the things she planned to do all through the Christmas season and wondered how it was possible to reconcile such things with the Holiest Time of All, the Birthday of the King. They discovered how her mind worked, how she thought only in terms of "me" and "my," and how all of her planning related to her own wishes and own desires. They even hovered close enough to perceive the yearnings of her heart, and could take no courage from what they found there.

And so it was with much trepidation and discouragement that they met again in their secret place to discuss their Problem Person and decide what in Heaven and on Earth could be done.

The First Little Angel was worried. "To get this Woman ready in time," she said, "will surely take a powerful lot of hovering."

The Second was likewise dubious. "How true you speak, Honey Angel. She is indeed far from being ready for the Birthday of the Babe."

The Third was plainly discouraged. "But what can we do to help her? She is missing the real meaning of Christmas."

But the Fourth had a suggestion. "Maybe if each one of us

could try to work on one thing she lacks, it would be more systematic and get better results."

"Of course," said the First. "That's what we'll do. I will work on her Loving Power. She does not know that Loving is the beginning of Christmas."

"Then I will work on her Giving Power," said the Second, "to teach her the joy of giving to those who need, for Giving is the joy of Christmas."

And the Third said, "I shall work on her Doing Power, for doing for others is the giving of one's self, and Doing is the happiness of Christmas."

Then the Fourth Little Angel said, "And that leaves me the Being Power. If I fail to make her grow into a better person because of the experience of Christmas, then all your work will be in vain."

And so the Christmas Cherubs agreed, and all went to work with might and main. They were so constant in their care and so determined in their desires, that the Problem Person was indeed besieged. She became the Perplexed, Pursued, Perturbed, and finally the Persuaded Problem Person. She found herself seeing many things that hitherto had completely escaped her—the chapped, rough red hands of the boy who brought her newspaper; the drenched burlap sacks wrapped around the feet of the old man who came to shovel snow; the happy, happy face of the Salvation Army girl who insistently rang the bell on the street.

She couldn't shut her ears to sounds that had never bothered her before—the silly, meaningless chatter of her hitherto all-important social functions; the long deep sigh that came from a child who stood outside a store window and looked in; the first-time beauty of the notes of "Silent Night" as she hurried home one evening. She even seemed to hear a most strange and unusual sound, like nothing she had ever heard before, almost like the hovering of angel wings.

At night she slept, but as she slept she dreamed the strangest dreams, and in the morning she awoke with new stirrings in her mind and new strivings in her soul. Oh, yes, the Christmas

Cherubs went wholeheartedly about their task, and cared so deeply about the results that when they were summoned to make their request for the Joyous Job of their choice, they had already agreed what their request would be. They stood before the Shining Radiance of the Throne of God and spoke their prayer as you and I are privileged to do.

"Dear Loving Father," said the First, "we have come to know the weakness of a woman's heart."

And the Second: "But we have also learned, O Father, the Goodness that can be made to grow there."

Then the Third: "O God, we had wanted to be Pullers of the Star, but now we agree that we should not leave off hovering, for Woman is a changing creature."

"And so, O King," prayed the Fourth, "we seek no other Joyous Job, for we have found joy in being needed, and Woman still needs our help."

And all four cherubs bowed their heads and said, "Amen." For that is the signal little children use to show their Father in Heaven that they have finished their prayers.

And God the Father, God the Son, God the Holy Spirit, heard the prayers of the Christmas Cherubs just as He hears the sincere prayers that come from you and me. And because God is Love, He loved the Christmas Cherubs for their angelic unselfishness. And because God is surprisingly good to His children, He gave the little angels far more than they asked, just as He gives to you and me. He gave them both of their Heart's Desires. He went Himself, in their place, just as He did in our place on Calvary, and He entered the heart of Woman, and His Holy Spirit dwelt therein all through the Blessed time of Christmas—and even dwells there still.

The Christmas Cherubs? Looking down, they perceived the work of the Holy Spirit, and knew then that God In Us can do far more than a multitude of hovering. And they were content about their Woman, and they were happy about their Joyous Job as they pulled the Christmas Star on the Night of Nights.

The Littlest Shepherd

by Dorothy D. Boulware

The darkness fell softly on the hillside over the muffled figures of the shepherds and the shadows that were the sheep. Campfires cast their flickering glow into the night and illumined the faces of the men who sat close to their friendly warmth. For a time there was a quietness upon them. Their evening meal was finished, their stories had been told, and their songs had died away across the slopes. It was a time for the memories of the old men and for the dreaming of the young. The dogs moved warily around the flock, their ears alert for the first sound of wolves that might creep silently and with deadly intent toward the unsuspecting sheep.

Overhead the stars gleamed with a fierce brilliance, piercing the darkness like a million shining windows to heaven. A cool breeze swept down from the hillside.

David did not see the flicker of the campfires or the brilliance of the stars, but he felt the coolness of the breeze and his ears were alert to the sounds of the camp. David could hear the silent advance of a wolf almost as soon as the dogs. He was aware of the first restless stirring of the sheep when they sensed that danger was near. His acute hearing told him where the shepherds lay or sat, and some special sense could always turn his face in the direction of his father. But David could not see as others see, for he was blind.

He was aware now that his father was coming toward him and knew ahead of time that his hand would fall gently upon his head as he said, "Time to sleep, my son, others will guard the sheep in the darkness." The words falling on his ears brought a protest now, as always, and David's clear voice rang out over the silent camp.

"I can hear the wolves more quickly than they can be seen, my father. May I not also take my turn at the night watch?" But his father with a tender smile spread his cloak upon the soft ground and lay his small son upon it, tucking the folds about him with gentle hands.

"Sleep well, my son; there will be many years for you to keep the night watch." Then he seated himself nearby and quiet returned again to the camp.

David waited until his father was occupied with his thoughts and then, carefully, he reached into the folds of his own cloak and pulled out a small stuffed lamb which had once been white and beautiful but which was now soiled and scarred by much love and many tears.

David was far too old to go to sleep with a toy. His father had told him so when he reached his sixth birthday. He had learned to keep it well hidden because the older lads had seen it and had teased him for clinging to it like a baby. Once they had grabbed the lamb and had thrown it from one to the other, laughing and shouting. Then, tiring of the sport, they had given it a toss which had taken it deep into a thorn bush. Only David's keen sense of hearing told him where it fell. When the lads left he crept into the bush and hunted until he found it hanging upon a thorn. His father, noticing the scratches, resolved that he must keep a closer watch on his son so that he would not stumble into the bushes. But David never told on his tormentors and thereafter he kept the lamb carefully hidden. Only at night did he pull it out and hold it tightly in his arms. He never guessed that his father during the lonely night saw the lamb and covered it with a fold of the cloak so that he might keep his secret.

His mother had made the lamb for him long ago when they had lived in happiness in a faraway village. She had made it of lamb's wool, bleached and carded, and had stuffed it with more wool so that it had indeed looked like the real lambs that gamboled on the hillside nearby. Bits of agate made its beady eyes, and its hooves were made of dried goatskin. She had even cut a strip of goatskin to make a collar and had attached a tiny bell, but the bell had long ago been lost. The lamb was white and fluffy and beautiful, and to the child who could not see it would always be beautiful.

The father, watching his small son, sighed and his eyes were full of sadness. Memories which slept during the day came rushing upon him in the darkness.

His son had not always been blind. He remembered the wonderful days when he had laughed and run and played like the other three-year-olds and then had gone to sleep in the arms of his mother as she sat on the doorstep of their home. How beautiful she had been, his Deborah, and how happy they were! He had had his own plot of ground and his own flock of sheep and the home which he had built for his beloved wife when they were married. Life was very sweet in those days and gave no forewarning of the tragedy that was to come. They had given praise to Jehovah for His bounty and had laughed and sung from morning to night.

One day a band of terrorists from the neighboring hills had advanced upon the countryside, burning homes, killing and pillaging. Benjamin, Deborah, and David had fled with their neighbors as the army approached. They were more fortunate than many of their friends, for scores were caught and killed and families were separated. They, however, were able to hide by day and make their way cautiously by night, journeying ever farther from the terror that had come upon them.

Finally they left the beautiful country with its sheltering trees and came to a vast desert. They had heard that on the other side of the desert there was a land much like their own had been, and so they turned their steps toward it. The traveling was not easy. No longer were they forced to journey by night for their pursuers were far behind them, but the sun beat down so fiercely that they were soon exhausted and could go but a short distance each day.

Throughout their hardships Deborah was patient and encouraging. They took turns carrying David, whose short legs soon tired. For a time they had found villages along the way where they could get food and lodging in exchange for work which Benjamin was able to do. There were wells where they could fill their goatskin flasks with water for the journey. But then they found themselves wandering where there were no wells and no villages. As the days passed their hardships increased. Their food was almost gone and only a small amount of water remained in the flasks. Once again they were traveling at night, avoiding the heat of the midday sun, but there was no shelter from its glare when they rested, and their skin was cracked and burned. David became feverish, and the last of the water had to be used to moisten his parched tongue. Deborah had been weakening gradually, but her courage was great.

The sandstorm that came upon them was the last blow. Benjamin had tried to protect them with his body as the hot and stinging sand forced its way into their mouths and nostrils and cut their skin like knives. When it was finally over the sun was sinking. Bruised and beaten he had picked himself out of the mound of sand that covered him. Deborah lay still, and it was with horror that he realized that in her weakened condition the storm had been too much for her. She had died quietly there amidst the driving sand, but she had placed David under her cloak and had shielded him so that he survived.

Heartbroken, Benjamin had picked the child up and had tried to wipe off the fine sand that had sifted through the coarse cloth of the cloak. David's eyes were full of it, but the toy lamb to which he had clung in his fright had protected his mouth and nose. It was some time before the child regained consciousness, and the realization that he could not see had come slowly but with a numbing finality to his father. With his blessed Deborah gone and his son blind it seemed to Benjamin that Jehovah had indeed deserted them. Weak from their hardships he could only lie on the sand with David clasped in his arms and wait to join his wife in death.

They did not know when the passing caravan came upon them and picked them up, for they were both unconscious. When Benjamin next opened his eyes he was in a house where kindly people ministered to him, placing cool cloths on his feverish head and urging him to sip some warm pottage. He struggled to rise until a wise old woman lifted his son up beside him.

"He has recovered more quickly than you, for he is young. He cannot see," she added gently, "but he has regained his strength and will live to make your heart glad again."

During the months that followed Benjamin slowly learned to live again. The land was indeed much like their own had been. He found the people kind and sympathetic. For many days he accepted their hospitality gratefully, but as his strength returned he did favors for them also. The villagers learned that he was a meticulous workman. He could make a table or mend a door or cut a window for their homes and he enjoyed working with his hands, which had never before been idle. Many of his newfound friends were thankful for the tasks he did to make their homes more comfortable or their labors easier. As time passed, however, Benjamin realized that he must make a home for himself and David and must seek some means of employment whereby they would no longer be dependent on the kindness of the people who had taken them in.

Opportunity came when he learned that a wealthy sheep owner was looking for another shepherd to help watch his flocks as they were driven to a distant hillside for better grazing. When Benjamin was given the job the friendly people with whom they had been staying begged him to leave David with them, but he could not part with his son. He knew that David must learn to live with his blindness but now needed the loving care of his father. And so David went along and became, in the joking words of the other shepherds, "the littlest shepherd" on the hillside.

The boy thrived on the outdoor life and loved his father's companionship. There were other shepherd lads, years older than he, but he did not miss having comrades his own age. His father was gentle, understanding, and firm. He taught David self-reliance, helped him to "see" through his fingertips and other senses so that now, after three years of a shepherd's life, it was sometimes hard to remember that he was blind. His radiant face, burned a deep brown by the sun, was turned expectantly and alertly to everything that went on in the camp. He learned to do many things to be helpful, and he was a happy child, healthier than he had ever been. He listened intently to the stories that were told about the fireside and became aware of the shepherds' faith in Jehovah and heard the thrilling prophecy of a Messiah who was promised to God's people. He thought often about the tales he heard and wondered with an intelligence far beyond his years how such things might come to pass. Only at night, when the quiet settled like a cloak upon the hillside, did a loneliness for the half-remembered touch of a mother's hand and the sound of her warm laughter and songs steal upon him and he would try to remember his mother's face. Then he would drift off to sleep and dream of her.

There was something different about this particular night—a feeling he could not put into words—a longing for something he could not understand. David hugged the lamb closely to him and rubbed its woolly sides. A large tear rolled slowly down his cheek, and he wondered why he was crying. Then he fell asleep and dreamed again of happiness.

David awoke suddenly to the sounds of a great confusion. The men were talking excitedly and the dogs were barking. The bleating of sheep came from the hillside. As he sat up David was aware of a light that pierced even the darkness in his eyes. Then, suddenly, there was silence. David jumped to his feet and made his way instinctively to his father's side. Benjamin was kneeling, and there was a strangeness about him that made David exclaim, "What is it, Father? What is it?"

"Hush, my son," whispered his father urgently, and David too became quiet and turned his face this way and that and called upon his sense of hearing to tell him what was happening.

Then, rolling across the hillside came a voice—a voice unlike anything David had ever heard. There was music in it and gentleness, and yet the tones reverberated across the hills like thunder. David quivered with expectation and excitement.

"Fear not: for, behold, I bring you good tidings of great joy, which shall be to all people. For unto you is born this day in the city of David a Saviour, which is Christ the Lord."

The Messiah! David knew at once what spell had come over them! He clutched his father's arm, but Benjamin shook him off and spoke not a word.

The Voice went on, "And this shall be a sign unto you; Ye shall find the babe wrapped in swaddling clothes, lying in a manger."

And then the air was filled with music. It filled David with ecstasy. Only the angels in heaven could sing so, he was sure. The music throbbed and swelled and reached every corner of the hills about them,

"Glory to God in the highest, and on earth peace, good will toward men."

David, too, had fallen to his knees, his upturned face enraptured. He was trembling with the beauty and grandeur of it all. And then, as suddenly as it had come, the music died away and for a moment there was complete silence. One by one the shepherds leaped to their feet, shouting excitedly to one another. Then one of the older shepherds called for quiet.

"Let us now go even unto Bethlehem, and see this thing which is come to pass, which the Lord hath made known unto us."

"The star," cried many voices; "see, it moves! Let us follow the star!"

And once again there was confusion as the men made ready to leave and David tried vainly to get his father's attention. All at once Benjamin paused.

"We cannot all go and leave the sheep untended upon the

hillside. Some must stay while others go and bring back word of this wondrous thing."

And so it was decided that they would cast lots and see who would make the journey and who would stay with the sheep. David tugged anxiously at his father's sleeve, but for once Benjamin was unaware of his son. When the lots had been cast David learned that his father was among those who were to go.

"Father! Father!" he cried. "May I go too? I want to go with you!" Benjamin, his attention gained at last, paused irresolutely as the men prepared to leave. He had never before left David alone.

"The journey will be far and tiring, my son," he said at last. "We must make haste, and it will be hard enough in the shadows for those who can see. You would not be able to keep up, and I cannot hurry with the others and carry you. I guess," he said slowly, "that you had best remain here with the others and help tend the sheep. I will hasten back and tell you all that I see." His hand rested gently on David's head for a moment, and then he hurried away to join the band of men who were already starting down the path and were calling impatiently.

David's heart was broken. More than anything else he wanted to be among those who visited the manger where the wondrous Babe lay. He drew a long sobbing breath. The camp was still full of excitement, and no one had time for a small boy who stood in the shadows.

Then a daring thought came to the boy. He was used to going along in the dark, trusting to his sense of feeling and hearing to direct him. He could easily follow the sound of the shepherds' voices and surprise his father when they arrived in Bethlehem. His father had sounded sad that he could not make the trip. He would let him know that he was getting bigger now and need not be carried. David felt sure his father would be proud that he had learned his lessons in self-reliance so well.

David moved quickly and started on a familiar path, hearing the voices of the shepherds clearly through the night. The way was not difficult. He had walked it many times with his father when they had taken the sheep to the far field to graze. He went rapidly along, his small shepherd's crook stretched out in front of him and his feet sure upon the path. He felt that he could never grow tired with the excitement and exhilaration pulsing through his veins. He could not see the star, but he almost thought he felt the warmth of its brilliance.

He had never been beyond the boundaries of the far field, however, and now the path became narrower and winding. Sometimes he could hear the voices of the men clearly. At other times they grew fainter, but he walked eagerly on. A turn in the path as it wound around the hillside brought the men directly below him and he could hear everything they said as if they were traveling together. They were discussing gifts. He had not thought about that. Of course there should be a gift for the birthday of the Baby! He listened intently. They had brought lambs to give the Child, and they had brought bags of carded wool to make His crib softer. They were lamenting that they had no richer gifts to offer. David's steps faltered a little. He could not go to see the Baby without a gift. What could he do? And then he had a thought which pleased him so that he skipped a step or two with satisfaction. In his excitement he was still holding the toy lamb. This would be his gift to the Baby—the most precious thing he possessed. The Baby would love its beautiful softness and would cling to it as He slept or played. As his father had told him, he was growing too old for it anyway. His eyes misted a little at the thought of giving it up, but he brushed the tears away and hurried on.

The trail became a little harder to follow. Several times he wandered to the side and the brambles and thorns caught at his clothing and scratched his face and arms painfully. Quickly he would make his way back to the path, straining his ears for the sound of the shepherds' voices now growing fainter all the time.

David's legs were beginning to ache, and he was getting very tired. He began to stumble, and several times he fell upon the rocks in the path. Each time it was harder to get up and go on. Finally he could deceive himself no longer. He could not hear at all the sound of the voices which had guided him, and he began to fear that he was completely lost. The sound of the wolves

howling in the distance frightened him, but even more important was the knowledge that he would not now see the Baby. He
sat dejectedly on the ground, not knowing which way to go. His
heart pounded wildly and the tears rolled down his cheeks. How
foolish he had been to attempt such a journey without his father's
hand to guide him!

"How I wish I, too, could see the star!" he sobbed. "If only the
angel would come back. He would show me the way to go."

Suddenly there was a sense of warmth through his body,
which had grown quite damp and chilled with the night air. It
seemed to him that he could see the brilliance of the star
through the darkness in his eyes, and he began to feel refreshed.
Once again he got to his feet and felt his way cautiously ahead.
Shortly thereafter he realized that his feet had found a road
which was hard-packed by the travel of many feet. He walked
on, relieved that the going had become easier. Then through the
silence he heard the clomp-clomp of camels' hooves. He went
quickly to the side of the road.

"What is this?" a man said, as the camels approached.

"A very small boy, Master, walking alone—why, he is blind."
The clomp-clomp of the camels' hooves stopped and David's
heart quickened.

"And whither do you go, my lad?" said a kindly voice. David
relaxed at the sound.

"I follow the star to see a Babe in a manger," said David
quickly. "I wanted to surprise my father, who has gone ahead
with a band of shepherds." His voice faltered with the last
words.

"No doubt he will be surprised," said the man dryly, "but I,
too, follow the star. Would you like to go with me?" He spoke to
the servant, who lifted David to the camel's back. David sighed
with relief as he leaned against the man.

"Did the angel send you?" he asked. There was a short silence,
then the man said slowly, "Who knows?"

As they went along the road the man who held David was
deep in thought. A "Wise One" they called him. Truly he had

studied the laws and prophecies for many years. Yet as they journeyed toward their destination he found himself beset by doubts. How could he believe that this was, indeed, the end of their long waiting. And how would they know for certain if the Baby who had just been born was the promised Messiah. True, the signs all pointed to the fulfillment of the prophecy, but there had been other disappointments.

The man sighed as he thought how full of hatred, greed, and war the world had become. Could they dare to believe that a Baby born under a new and flaming star would bring peace to the hearts of men? He wondered if his companions, wise and noble though they were, could be sharing his doubts at the moment.

"Did the angel send you?" the child had asked. Well, he himself had seen no angel. He had seen only a star, newly shining in the sky, and with his companions had dared to find hope in his heart. But the journey from the East had been tiring. Now, at last, would they find that it was all in vain? If only by some miracle there would be absolute proof that this was, indeed, the long-awaited Messiah. A miracle! The man shrugged a shoulder. The day for miracles was long past.

Wearily he shifted the boy's weight and smiled to see that his little friend had fallen into an exhausted sleep, lulled by the swaying of the camel. Why could not he, the Wise One, believe as trustfully as this child, who, blind though he was, had started out alone to find the Baby in a manger? Well, perhaps there would be a miracle. Perhaps at the end of the journey they would be sure.

When David awoke he knew that they had reached their destination. He heard voices and the lowing of cattle and the bleating of sheep. The man handed him down to the servant, who set him on his feet.

The little boy's clothes were torn to rags. His hair was full of thorns. The tears and dust had made muddy furrows on his cheeks. He still clutched the lamb, which had received its added share of dirt and grime. He stood still, listening, and then he went toward the sounds. He did not hear his father's voice and for a moment this disconcerted him. Then, drawn as if by a magnet, he made his way to the doorway of a stable.

David felt a warmth like the rays of the sun upon him. He pushed against the bodies of the men who were crowding the doorway. Then, stooping, he darted between their legs until he felt himself in a clearing. He drew in his breath and smelled the clean hay and the odor of animals. There was another fragrance that came to David's sensitive nostrils. It was faint and sweet and stirred memories half-forgotten of a mother who had held him in her arms as she crooned lullabies.

David was a tired little boy. The memories were overpowering. The tears once more started down his cheeks. He could feel people looking at him and he thought he heard a gasp from the crowd.

"The Baby—," he stammered. "I came to find the Baby." Then a voice which was like nothing David had heard since his mother died spoke softly in the silence.

"Why, it is a little boy," the voice said. "Come here, my dear." And moving slowly further into the radiant warmth David went toward the voice as if in a dream. He felt the softness of a dress and the greater softness of a gentle hand.

Behind him David was sure he heard a gasp this time and an exclamation: "David!" It was his father's voice, incredulous and horrified, but somehow nothing mattered to David now except the miracle that was happening. Restraining hands reached for him, but the softer hands drew him closer. The beautiful voice said, "Why, he's hurt. Bring me cloths that I may dress his wounds." Then, gently, the woman whom he could not see lifted a corner of her robe and wiped the small, dirty face and dried the tears, which were streaming faster now.

"There," she said, "there. It is all right. Don't cry. This is a night for rejoicing."

David's heart was soothed as he pressed close to her. "Are you a mother?" he asked. "I had a mother once. I wish I could see a mother again." From behind them in the darkness a sob broke from a man's throat.

"Yes," said the voice, and the music of all the angels was in it, "I am a mother." And she clasped the small boy to her. For a moment he rested his weary head against the softness of her breast. Then he looked up.

"The Baby," he said again, "I came to find the Baby. I brought Him a gift. It is a beautiful lamb. My mother made it for me long ago." And he raised the dirty and bedraggled lamb from his cloak.

"David!" his father was indeed horrified now, but David paid no heed. The mother took the lamb gently from his hands.

"It is indeed a lovely gift, my son," she said; "the Baby will treasure it always." And to the amazement of the watchers she tenderly placed the lamb in the Baby's arms. Then, suddenly, no one quite knew how, the lamb gleamed as white as snow. Its agate eyes sparkled in the light and it was softer than down. Only David was not surprised because he did not see. The Babe smiled and clutched the lamb tightly.

"And now," said the mother, "would you like to kiss the Baby to whom you gave your lamb?"

"Oh, yes!" said David. "How I wish that I might see Him!" He leaned solemnly over, feeling for the edge of the manger, and as he did so one of the Baby's hands brushed softly against David's face.

Suddenly there was a blinding light in David's eyes. He straightened up and covered them with his hands. When he took them away he looked upon the face of the mother, who smiled. Then he turned to the Baby, who lay with the woolly lamb held tightly against Him, and He also smiled. David leaned toward the crib and looked with love and wonder at the Babe he had so longed to see. As he raised his eyes he was aware that kneeling beside him at the manger there was a man in kingly robes who extended his gift of gold while the tears ran down his cheeks.

"The faith of a little child—," the man murmured, but David was so full of happiness that he did not try to understand.

Then he turned his eyes toward the shepherds who were crowded in the doorway and found his father's face. Benjamin was crying, but his tears were those of joy, David knew. For a moment their eyes met in a look of love and understanding. David turned back to the Baby and looked at the beautiful little white lamb in His arms. He tried to speak, but his heart was too full of happiness for the words to come.

The angels bending down from heaven sang and the music found an echo in the depths of David's heart. The night was filled with the beauty of all the ages, for it was the First Christmas—and the beginning of a new life for the littlest shepherd.

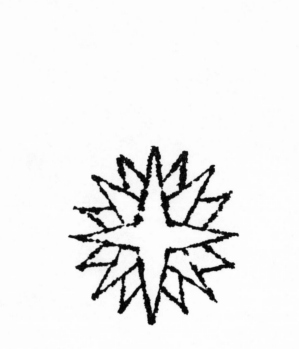

A Star Is Born

by Kenneth G. Phifer

It was the year 70 A.D. The city of Jerusalem was in turmoil. The revolt against the authority of Rome had proceeded well at first, but now the end of Jewish hopes seemed at hand. Outside the city walls were the armies of Titus, fully equipped, well trained, veterans of many campaigns, confident and well fed. Inside the walls was a disorderly mob, under inadequate leadership, with few weapons—and hunger.

Joseph, the physician, turned wearily from the streets to pause for a moment's rest on the temple steps. When one is hungry one's energy vanishes like a fleeting shadow, he thought grimly. Joseph's head swam a little and he dropped it on his hand until the swimming stopped. When he raised it he realized that someone else was there. Not three feet away sat a man. It was Nahum of Bethany, his younger colleague and friend. Strange that Nahum had said no word when he came up. The darkness of midnight was lying over the temple, to be sure, but it was not so dark that one could not recognize a friend. It was strange that Nahum said no word now, simply sat and stared into the night.

"Nahum," Joseph called softly. There was no answer. "Nahum," he repeated in louder tones. Slowly the younger man turned his head. His unseeing eyes rested blankly on Joseph for a moment. Then he spoke, almost as if to himself.

"Joseph, I have just seen a woman die. Oh! I know, I've seen women die before—and children and strong men. But this is one death I cannot forget. It was from hunger, really, as so many now are dying. 'Twas not the manner or the cause but the way she smiled, and what she said, and the way she walked the awful road of death without a word of fear.

" 'Tis strange. I am a doctor and have seen unusual things before, have heard strange tales; but this was different. It seems I cannot shake it from my mind; it is like the memory of warmth when one is chilled. The ringing certainty in that woman's voice, the joy in her eyes as she told that story to me—I can't forget them.

"I can't forget her words when I told her there was nothing more that I could do, that it was too late, and when I asked if she was afraid to die. There was real wonder in her eyes. 'Afraid? No, I am not afraid. In the darkness of an old stable behind my father's inn one morning just before the dawn, many, many dawns ago when I was just a little girl, I slipped one trembling, cautious finger into the soft palm of a newborn baby, and I've never been afraid, really, since then. Because of that, now in the darkness just before another dawn, I can slip my hand into the hand of God and—no, I am not afraid.'

"She said it just as calmly as though she were remarking upon the fact of my presence, but within her eyes those strange star flowers suddenly bloomed that sometimes make a woman's eyes like the eyes of an angel. Suddenly I wanted to hear this woman's story. She must have read the eagerness upon my face.

" 'My name is Rachel,' she said. 'My father kept an inn in Bethlehem, a very little inn, for Bethlehem is a very little town. But once it was large for a night, larger than anyone ever knew, for it held the very center of the universe in one of its stables. From Rome had come the word that all the inhabitants of earth should be enrolled for purposes of taxation. Not only was everyone to be enrolled, but each was to be enrolled in the town from whence he had come. So on the night of which I speak they were pouring in from all parts of Palestine, returning home. Rich merchants who were haughty and arrogant, poor unsuccessful men who were meek and submissive, old men to whom life now meant just remembering, young men for whom it meant hoping, good men, bad men, women, children. Like some mighty stream they flowed in. I ran excitedly from one corner of the court- yard to another. Now and then I would stop and talk shyly to some child.

" 'Father was so busy he did not even notice me until the night had crept into every nook and cranny of the courtyard. The noise was growing, coarse and rowdy now, and when I next stumbled across Father's path he ordered me, in tones I did not dare to question, into the house. I turned quickly, so quickly that I did not see the man behind me until I crashed into him, full tilt, and was seated on the ground. He picked me up with grave courtesy, and as he brushed the dust from my clothes laughed a little, but there was not much humor in his laugh, just a great weariness. "I'm looking for the innkeeper, little girl," he said. "He's my father. There he is," I replied. "Thank you, my child." He began to shoulder his way through the crowd, his body towering above the mob.

" 'I watched him for a moment, then ran to the door of the inn. Mother stood there, her face troubled as she talked to a girl who leaned wearily against the door, one soft hand resting lightly upon the neck of the little donkey on which she had been riding. "No, we have no room in the inn," Mother was saying. The young woman's face was suddenly drawn and tired. There were little creases of pain about her mouth. She could not hide the disappointment in her eyes, in the slump of her shoulders. Then the man I had bumped into was there, his long arm around her, his smile struggling through the cloud of worry on his face. "Do not despair, my little Mary. We will find a place." When he looked at her it was as if he spoke, and when he spoke it was as if he sang a hymn of love. It was plain that he loved her so, this gentle, quiet-faced woman in the peasant garb. Instinctively I liked these clean, quiet people. An idea burst upon my brain and I tugged at my mother's skirt, "There is the stable. It is clean and warm; and I saw Reuben putting fresh straw in the manger not an hour ago." Mother looked at me gratefully, then to the travelers she said, "The child speaks true, and you are welcome." Her glance turned to the woman and softened in womanly sympathy. "Stay here, my dear." Then she sent me to bed.

" 'I lay in my room high above the courtyard and my thoughts paraded past against the background of the hum of human activity below. Through the window above my bed the stars peeped in, those eternal candles of God with which He looks into the darkness of children's bedrooms everywhere and makes sure that they are safe. I got up and looked out. There was that great star that I had seen every night for months. Larger and whiter than all the rest, it had hovered on the horizon before, but tonight it had moved upon the canopy of the sky until it was—why, it was just above our stable! I felt that if I were on the stable roof I could reach out my hand and touch that star. I shivered joyfully. Everyone wants to touch a star, and that was the most beautiful I had ever seen. Queer that it should hang just there! But then the whole atmosphere of that night was queer. It was soft like a perfumed breath, close like an encircling arm; no breeze, yet the air gave the impression of some haunting, whispering melody somewhere. I sighed and climbed back into bed. Sleep slowly pulled a curtain over the moving panorama of my thoughts; and the last thing I remembered was the star.

" 'When I awoke it was the first thing I thought of, for my room was filled with a white light that I knew was not the dawn. I sat up in bed, and there was the star still hanging above the stable, but greater, brighter, and more beautiful even than it had been before. It seemed about to burst with the fullness of its glory, and from the stable suddenly came the thin, fluttering cry of a baby. Impulsively I dressed and ran downstairs. From the tops of the distant mountains dawn was hanging lacy fringes on the edges of night's black curtain. Instinctively I changed my headlong run into hushed, awed footsteps as I

entered the stable door. The cry rang out again and I saw the
baby lying in a manger. I saw no one but that child and began
to move silently toward it. With some unknown fear clutching
my heart, I knelt beside the strange crib. Then I felt Mother's
hand upon my shoulder. "The angels came last night and left
this baby here for Mary and Joseph." "They came upon the
beams of the star, I'm sure," I cried. Mother smiled, but Mary
spoke almost as though she were alone, "Yes, they came upon
the beams of the star. This night a Star is born, the Star of David, and the light of it shall be for the healing of the nations."
Then she bowed her head and I thought she prayed. I looked
around and saw that there were others in the room, strange men
dressed like shepherds, Joseph, Father. But my eyes went always back to the baby. He held my attention by some strange,
fascinating power. Still there was that fear, until I put out a
cautious finger and laid it on His little palm. It was the softest
palm. I do believe He tried to clutch my finger, and I thought
He smiled. That clutch tore away all the fear from around my
childish heart, and that smile has made life look bright for me
ever since. I crept slowly from the stable to think on the wonder
of God's gift. The star had faded into the red glory of the rising
sun which caught the bare, outstretched arms of an old tree and
threw a gigantic, grotesque cross athwart the courtyard.

"'You have lived in Palestine and surely you have heard the
rest—how He grew up, this child of Bethlehem, and lived for
good and truth and honor; how He came to place those baby
hands, now grown strong and powerful, upon the sick and suffering among our people, and healed them. That is how some
like to remember Him—as the good Physician. You have heard
surely how He reached those delicate, tender fingers down to
the very soul of our nation and quickened it to life. That is how
some like to remember Him, as the greatest of the Prophets.
You have heard, too, how they took those hands at last and
drove great nails through the palms and hanged Him on a tree.
That is what some remember best—a young man agonizing on a
cross. Then you know how it was told that He arose and appeared unto His friends and lifted those hands over them at last

in benediction and farewell, and told them theirs was a world to conquer in His name. That is what some remember—a risen, victorious, glorified Lord. But I am a simple Christian, sir, who remembers best a little Baby lying in a manger, a Baby whose palm was very soft and whose mother was very beautiful.'

"The woman's voice trailed into silence. All the time she had been speaking God had been lighting the stars one by one. The sky looked very low and close to the window. Her eyes were fast becoming glazed, but she smiled as if she saw something I could not—smiled and put out one finger as though she reverently felt something there before her. Her lips moved and I bent low to hear her words, 'That night a Star was born.' Then she died. It is strange, but just as the light went out in her eyes a star was born. It flashed out in glorious, unexcelled brilliance so that momentarily it lighted up the room. It was uncanny, I say, and I deal with bodies, not with spirits and souls. You know I deal not in religion and in superstition. Still 'tis strange, Joseph, strange and beautiful, and I cannot shake it from my mind.

"They are there outside the gates of Jerusalem tonight. Their hungry swords are sharp and bright, Roman swords lusting for Jewish blood. We are told there is no help. Yet, when despair traces her black pictures in my mind, I see a Star that lighted up a woman's death. It gives promise of another life. Suppose it is all true! Suppose God has entered into life, that Jehovah of Hosts has entered man's tragedy. Suppose He suffers with His children. More! Suppose He transforms man's tragedy, and that a star is always born in moments of blackness to be seen only by those who lift their eyes and trust. Suppose this world will die but to have a new birth, a finer life. Suppose we individuals die but to live again. And suppose force is not all, but that there are finer, stronger things like love and hope; enduring simple things like flowers and trees and the birth of children and of stars. 'Tis strange, but this night I have found a faith. My faith is that all the tramping, marching feet of all the soldiers can never trample out a Star that gleams even brighter at death, never crush the might of a Baby's hand that can lead a woman through a life."

Incident
in a Minor Province

by Jack Abernathy

Perhaps Quintus Severus shouldn't have taken that second cup of wine at the inn. But if there had been no lingering at the table, he would have been halfway across Bethlehem when it happened.

And if there had been no cool fire playing across his tired muscles, he would not have acted so hastily. That cursed caution, which plagued him at every decisive turn (and kept him only a corporal after twenty years in the Tenth Legion), would have kept him from . . . ah, the world's history turns on such "might-have-been's."

But listen to this story, and you may judge for yourself of its import.

Winter's chilly sun plunged toward the horizon. Within an hour it would be dark again in this dust-choked Judean village. Another day gone, only ten left until the first of the month Janus. Then the census could be taken, the tax rolls fully prepared, and it would all be over. Over, that is, except for Quintus Severus and his two maniples of legionaries on traffic control. They would still have to get all these Judeans back on the road home.

"Praise be to all the gods from Jupiter on down and sideways," Quintus thought, "my plan has worked well." It all seemed absurdly easy now. No animals allowed on the main street, which was part of the highway from Jerusalem to Hebron. Instead, traffic going south kept to the west side of the city, while northbound traffic took the east side. Soldiers at each gate kept things moving.

"There's no trouble from the animals," Quintus mused; "at least, not as much as you get from people. Animals have so much more wisdom than humans. Particularly these pesky Judeans, who seem to love nothing more than the sound of their own voices, and milling about in the streets."

The street noises swelled then, and dropped, as a tall man entered and pushed his way past Severus to the landlord's stall. Quintus took up his clay mug for a final swallow, and heard two strange notes outside. One was the ringing "clop-clop" of horses, the other a rising babble of shouts and cries.

Both sounds spelled trouble to his soldier ears. His legs had carried Severus to the door almost before he knew it. In the seconds it took to fling open the door, his eyes scanned the confused scene before him and darted to its cause.

Two men were pulling at a donkey's halter, but in opposite directions. Ears laid back, eyes rolling in fear, the animal had three feet firmly planted on the cobbled street. The fourth leg was tangled in the ropes of some baggage against the inn wall. With the donkey's quivering length, the burly pair hauling at him, and the press of onlookers, Bethlehem's main street was thoroughly blocked.

At that instant a Roman soldier flung himself off his horse, drawing his short sword as he strode toward the donkey. Quintus had already plucked a knife from his boot sheath to cut the animal loose. Then he realized the soldier meant to use the blade to force the donkey aside.

The crowd gasped, and the two men dropped the donkey's halter as the soldier moved in. Three quick strides brought Quintus to his side unnoticed. His clenched fist smashed down on the soldier's wrist, the knife scraped across knuckles, and Quintus' boot crashed into his opponent's shinbone.

Curses spilled out as the soldier scrambled for his sword, but Quintus had moved on. Two slashes freed the imprisoned leg. As he put up his knife, the corporal moved to the donkey's head. Grasping the animal's ears, he pulled them forward. Blocking the donkey's vision and clucking to him softly, Quintus half pushed and half led him into a niche. A stocky man with a calm face stepped forward and took the tether.

Quintus turned, anger mounting within him at the two violations of his rules. Absorbed in shifting the donkey, he had not noticed the approach of another horse and rider. Startled, he reached for his sword.

"What is this, soldier? Would you draw your weapon against me?" The voice was a woman's, the face he recognized slowly as his anger drained. It was Messalia, wife of Magnius Felix, procurator of Judea. Quintus very nearly stammered as caution surged over him again.

"Your pardon, Procuratrix. I did not know you were in Bethlehem. I feared an attack from the soldier I struck just now. It would be the furtherest thing from my mind to . . ."

"Never mind. What is your name, and your duties here?"

"Quintus Severus, corporal, Tenth Legion. I am charged with directing the traffic through here, and maintaining order in the streets."

"You call this *order*," the procuratrix cut in. "You allow this stupid donkey to block the highway and stir up the beginnings of a riot. You attack one of my escorts with a knife. What is worse, Corporal Severus, your men tried to send me off on a dirty side street back at the gates."

"But this donkey is here against my orders. And I struck the soldier with my fist—the knife was an accident." Quintus did not dare point out that the Lady Messalia herself had added to the uproar.

"Let us have no excuses, soldier. We must reach Jerusalem before nightfall or I would have the centurion in charge arrest you. I shall see that my husband hears of this. You had better make a full investigation of this incident, and a complete report. Tell the centurion to send it directly to the Procurator."

"It shall be done, Procuratrix." Quintus felt his shoulders sag.

"Now clear out this rabble of Judeans, corporal, before my men let them feel their sword points." Messalia jerked at her reins and signaled her escort to move on.

Quintus shouted in Aramaic to the crowd, and the moving horses did the rest. In a few minutes the party trotted out of sight around a bend in the street.

Wearily the corporal turned back to where he had left the donkey. Two men stood beside it, and a woman sat on its wooden saddle. Her shoulders drooped a bit, but her face shone quietly behind the folds of her shawl. Something about her seemed familiar.

Then Quintus recognized the tall man who had hurried into the hostel just before the trouble. Obviously he was the owner of the donkey and the source of the afternoon's calamities. Frustration welled up inside the corporal, but something held back his powerful fists. Perhaps it was his glimpse of the woman's face, perhaps his inborn caution.

Nothing held back his tongue, however.

"You flea-brained, blundering idiot," Quintus blurted as the stranger turned to face him. "Who do you think you are? Breaking Roman traffic laws, halting the Lady Messalia and her party, and now you stand calmly chatting as if nothing had happened. I'm the one who will pay for this. Before the week's out, I'll be busted to private, rear rank, perhaps flogged—and lucky if it stops there. Well, come on, man, speak up—and make it good."

For a moment there was silence. Then the man's voice sounded —grave, yet courteous.

"You asked who I am. If there were time, I should indeed welcome the opportunity to tell you—for I am made of a thousand elements, even as you. But time presses, and . . ."

"We have all the time we need," Quintus broke in. "I mean to make you sweat for this. We have a guardhouse for trouble-makers."

"I have not helped you to see." The man was still unruffled.

"Let me introduce you to my wife, Mary. Perhaps you have not noticed that she is with child. Our five days' journey from Nazareth has been difficult for her, and her time is near. If you will allow me to see her taken care of as quickly as possible, then you may do with me what you like, if it be justice."

Now Quintus fell silent, for long minutes. "That explains the donkey, then, and does you credit." His voice was oddly husky. "But why have you not taken her into the inn?"

"There is no room," the husband answered. "They told us so at the gate, but I knew not where else to seek. We trusted in the mercies of Yahweh, our living God, and prayed to Him. I am sure it is His providence that has sent us this man of Bethlehem."

"How can he help? Every house in town is jammed."

"Indeed you are right, sir. And Geshur here says his own home is filled with relatives. But he has offered us the shelter of his stable, dug into the hillside under this inn. And with the help of his good woman for my wife, under God's tender care we shall be safe."

"So you shall." Quintus' voice was hard again. "You shall have a guard to keep you under my thumb. For now, take care of your wife—and your child. Lead them away, Geshur."

Three days passed before Quintus came to the cave stable. Much had happened, and his face was that of a man whose future trembled in the balance. Even in the confusion of the census, Roman military justice must be carried out swiftly—particularly when the Procurator's wife chose to get involved

No Roman guard was in sight as Quintus neared the stable. There were only small knots of Judeans whose talk dropped off as the corporal passed. A husky, half-bearded youth sat by the door, mending a broken ox yoke.

"Look here, boy," Quintus called. "Where's the guard? And who in the name of Mars are you?"

"The guards quit yesterday when the Centurion Tiberius sent them off to work the gates." The young man stood. "I am called Lamech, and my duties are to serve as a stable hand to Geshur, the owner."

"Is that Galilean still here, with his wife?"

"You mean Joseph and Mary. They are, and the child, too."
Lamech's features altered, lit with a pulse of joy

"The child is born, then." Quintus spoke almost to himself.
"How is he? I mean, is the child . . ."

"He is marvelous beyond words, corporal. Though still bound
in the swaddling clothes, he seems to radiate strength, yet a
strength that is peace itself. I believe that he shall be our longed-
for Messiah. In your tongue, the word is Savior—one who can
save you, lift you up and out of yourself into something far
nobler than ever you dreamed."

"What are you babbling of?" Quintus seemed staggered by
the idea. "A child Savior—nonsense!"

"Nay, it makes more sense than anything I have ever heard.
Last night, after he was born, a band of shepherds knocked at
the door. To Joseph they told their tale of a mighty vision, but
I heard too. An angel of the Lord God, Yahweh, appeared and
spoke to them of a child born that day in Bethlehem who is to
be the Messiah, the Savior. As a sign, they would find the babe
wrapped in swaddling clothes, lying in a manger. More than that,
they were nearly blinded by a great light as of the glory of the
presence of God. Yet they could see and hear a multitude of the
hosts of heaven itself singing praises to God. Do you know what
they sang of, corporal?"

"Say on, stable hand," Quintus breathed.

"They sang of peace. Peace, corporal. And of good will to
men. Is that not a vision worth following? A vision even worth
dying for?"

Quintus shuddered, and squared his shoulders. "I thank you,
Lamech, for these words. I shall think on them. Now let me see
this child and his parents."

Inside, there seemed to be no need for words. Long the corporal looked upon this strange child, the Son of a strange kind
of god, and his mother. Finally he roused himself and, beckon-
ing to Joseph, walked purposefully to the door.

He spoke in low tones. "Look you, Joseph. I came here intend-
ing to take you to Jerusalem with me. I have had my hearing
before Procurator Felix himself. It seems I am charged with the

grave crime of allowing a great Roman lady to be put to the indignity of halting for a small donkey and a group of lowly Judeans. Actually, there is more to the history of the Lady Messalia's dislike for me."

Quintus paused. "But the issue was put to me thus. If I would lay the fault to you and bring you to trial at Jerusalem, the charge would be dismissed. In effect, if I would betray a Judean, I could go free. Otherwise, I shall suffer the punishment."

"Many things I understand now," Joseph said. "But what is the point of forcing you to deliver up a member of the race of Israel?"

Quintus looked beyond Joseph into the past. "For forty years I was alone in the world. Two years ago I met a woman from Nazareth. We belonged together, and we were married in Jerusalem. Yes, you may have heard the story. At any rate, Magnius Felix frowns on that sort of thing, and his wife . . . to say she despises such marriages is putting it mildly."

Again Quintus paused. "Veterans like me are hard to come by, though. And I have such a way with animals that I am useful for projects like the Syrian legate's proposed camel troop. But this was the breaking point."

"And your decision?" Joseph was calm as always.

"This child and his peace have helped me choose. I will suffer Roman justice before I betray any man again." Quintus opened the door. "It was just one year ago today that my wife and child died for lack of human help. God be with you, Joseph."

"We shall pray for your soul each day," Joseph called. But the corporal had vanished into the dusk.

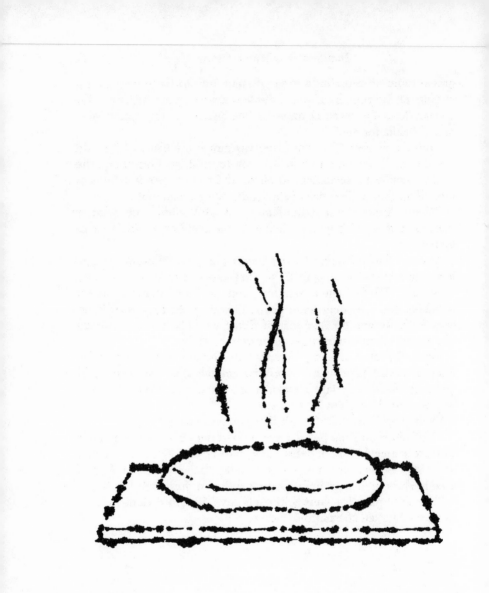

Butter and Honey

by Katharine Allyn See

Long shadows were falling across the street of Nazareth. From the carpenter's shop there still came the sound of hammer and plane. In the little room next to the shop three people were busily using the last rays of sunlight that came through the narrow window. The mother was mending. Little Brother was studiously forming letters with a bit of charcoal on a tile. Little Sister was scurrying about, tidying the room.

"I *can* cook," Little Sister told her brother. "Today I made a cake; not just an ordinary cake, but one with butter and honey in it."

"Butter and honey?" he echoed.

"With butter and honey," she repeated. She put her hand over her lips as the hammering stopped in the next room; glancing at the door she continued, whispering until the sound began again. "It's a very special cake, for Big Brother, because tomorrow is his birthday."

"Butter and honey . . . tomorrow is his birthday. . . ." Where had she heard those words? "Butter and honey." The mother pondered them until she remembered:

"Behold, a virgin shall . . . bear a son, and shall call his name

Immanuel. Butter and honey shall he eat." Her hands lay idle in her lap as memory after memory came back to her. Little Sister's startled voice broke in upon her thoughts.

"Mother! You must be thinking about angels! Your face is all— shining."

She could not speak aloud the glory she had been remembering. She only smiled and said, "Your cake was made well, and it will please Big Brother very much."

She took up her needle again and Little Sister her broom. The tap-tap of the hammer came from the carpenter's shop. At length the girl spoke again:

"Mother, I'm sure that some day Big Brother is going to do something very wonderful, aren't you?"

"Of course I'm sure," the mother answered; then added quickly, "but you know mothers always feel that way."

(For how could she speak what she, blessed above all mothers, *knew*? How could she put in words the tender memories and the shining promises that filled her heart?)

Again there was silence, broken only by the sound of the hammer.

Down the village street, through the lengthening shadows, a figure came stumbling; and as he moved he cried aloud:

"I am hungry; give me meat! I am thirsty; give me drink!"

Little Brother looked up from the work in his lap. "A beggarman is coming," he said.

Little Sister climbed to the window. "Mother," she reported, "he's lame, or sick. And his clothes are all torn."

"I am hungry; give me meat!" came the cry of the beggarman. "I was in prison; minister to me."

"Oh, Mother!" the small girl exclaimed in a tone of pity. "He says he was in prison. Can't we give him something?"

The mother looked anxiously toward the cupboard. "I think we can give him something," she replied, "but we haven't much."

"Wait!" said the child. "I'll go ask Big Brother what *he* thinks. Listen. He's stopped hammering; maybe he hears the beggarman, too."

Little Brother looked soberly after her as she disappeared through the door of the shop. "Big Brother will say yes," he said. "He'd rather be hungry himself than not give to somebody else. Why is that, Mother?"

She answered thoughtfully, "Because it hurts him when other people are hungry, or hurt, or sad, or wicked. It hurts him more than being hungry or tired himself." She rose and lighted the small earthenware lamp and set it on its bracket.

"I am hungry; give me meat!" came the cry of the beggarman, outside the door.

The tap of the hammer began again as Little Sister came hurrying back. "Big Brother says," she announced, "'Share our food, in the name of God.'" She hunted through the cupboard, then ran into the street. They heard her clear, high voice, and the hoarse tones of the beggarman. Then slowly she came back, closing the door behind her.

The mother moved quietly about the room, preparing supper. Little Brother put away his tile and charcoal. But Little Sister only sat in the corner of the room, not speaking a word. The others watched her, puzzled. "What is your trouble, Little Sister?" the mother asked at length.

The girl ran to her, hid her face, and broke out into tears. "I wish I hadn't done it!" she sobbed. "I gave the butter-and-honey cake to the beggarman."

"You gave away the butter-and-honey cake!" cried Little Brother in distress. "But what will Big Brother have for his birthday?"

"I thought he'd be so pleased if I gave it away," she answered, still sobbing. "But now I can't give it to *him*."

The mother stroked her hair comfortingly. "Go tell Big Brother you made it for him," she said. "He'll still be pleased."

Little Sister passed through the door of the shop, and for a long time the hammer was silent. Then it began again, and she came dancing back into the room, her eyes shining through the last few teardrops.

"I *did* give it to him, Mother!" she exclaimed. "I did after all. Do you know how? Well, if I do something for somebody who needs it, because I love Big Brother, why, that's just like doing it to Big Brother himself. He said so."

But the mother did not answer, only there was again the shining look in her face. For her heart was saying,

"*Behold, a virgin shall . . . bear a son, and shall call his name Immanuel—God with us.*"

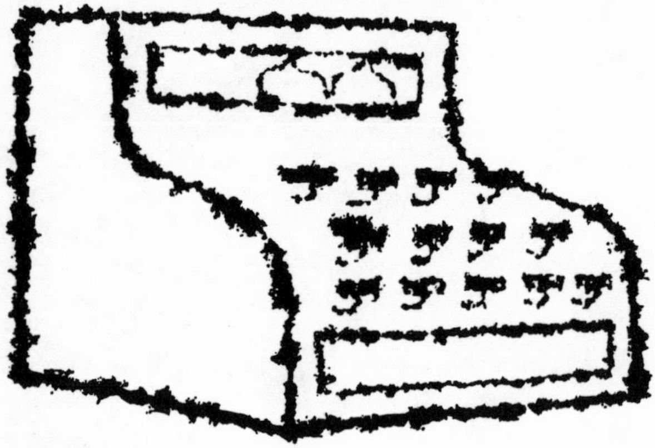

Mr. Jones Goes to Bethlehem

by Harmon B. Ramsey

Mr. Jones was a most cantankerous old codger. He was testy, disagreeable, argumentative, and belligerent. He ruled over Paramount Department Store, Incorporated, like a martinet.

Besides, he was stingy.

Prying a contribution out of him for church or charity was the most unwelcome assignment any man in the community could receive. Mr. Jones was most liberal with his criticisms and most parsimonious with his gifts. Any solicitor for charity could expect to be subjected to a torrent of abuse and invective toward the cause he represented, so that when Mr. Jones finally consented to write a small check he made himself appear virtuous for giving anything at all to a cause that he had proved, at least to himself, to be so manifestly undeserving.

If you had peeped into the Recording Angel's dossier on Mr. Jones you could have expected to see such entries as these:

Mr. Jones's wife (on numerous occasions): "I do declare, if that man would just once admit that he was wrong . . . but it's always somebody else's fault."

Mr. Jones's assistant manager (remark made upon being questioned by one of the clerks): "I must confess that at times Mr. Jones is a bit trying." *(The assistant manager is noted for his kindness and patience, so his words may be interpreted as a gross understatement.)*

Mr. Jones's secretary: "Mr. Jones is positively the lousiest guy I ever worked for!"

Under "Typical Instances of Behavior":

When the Community Chest canvasser called, Mr. Jones checked the canvasser's account at the store and upon finding him two months behind in the payment of his bill so soundly berated him that the embarrassed canvasser did not press his appeal for a contribution to the Chest.

Under "Helpful Deeds Performed":

No items worth mentioning.

In short, Mr. Jones was impossible.

But an explanation is due and must not be further delayed. All that has been said describes the Mr. Jones that *was*. This is the Mr. Jones men knew before he made his journey to Bethlehem. How Mr. Jones became a different Mr. Jones is the point of our story.

I

It happened, as may be guessed, at Christmas time. This was one season of the year when a slight manifestation of the milk of human kindness appeared in Mr. Jones's nature. It was not enough to make any appreciable alteration in the familiar outlines of his character, but it at least gave some hint of what a decent sort of fellow Mr. Jones might be if he let himself go. He had smiles for his clerks and office force and was perceptibly less critical. But he was the same Mr. Jones for all that.

It probably happened—this thing that did happen to Mr. Jones—at Christmas because he was more responsive then to the spiritual influences that beat upon our lives.

Mr. Jones is standing outside the department store admiring the appealing Christmas scene which he has instructed his window designer to feature during the holiday season. There is the Christ Child in the manger, with His mother and Joseph nearby. The shepherds are kneeling in adoration, and in the distance the Wise Men may be seen approaching.

The window designer has done his work with skill, and many in the crowds of shoppers have paused in their hurrying from store to store to draw inspiration from the scene. Mr. Jones himself is moved by it. His feeling is partly pride that it is *his* store which is attracting attention and partly the warm glow kindled by the simple Christmas story.

Mr. Jones turns from the window with a kindly expression on his face and an appreciative ear for the Christmas carol that is heard from the chimes of a nearby church. Absorbed in these pleasant thoughts of Christmas, Mr. Jones begins to stride across the street in his usual aggressive manner but with his mind oblivious of the congested condition of the traffic. There is the sudden sound of alarm from an automobile horn as Mr. Jones steps squarely into the path of the oncoming car. A cry rises from the crowded streets as Mr. Jones goes down. An ambulance quickly appears, and Mr. Jones is expertly lifted to a stretcher and sped to the hospital.

Mr. Jones's physical form is off to the hospital, where his injuries will be well taken care of and where it will be discovered that he is not seriously hurt. More interesting to us is the journey which Mr. Jones's mind takes while he lies unconscious in the ambulance and later at the hospital.

II

Back across the centuries and out across the miles goes Mr. Jones until he finds himself in surroundings that have a faint familiarity. He is among a group of shepherds in Judea at night.

Now he remembers, and he knows exactly what is going to happen. Presently an angel will appear standing by them, surrounded by a great light. The shepherds will become alarmed until the angel calms their fears and says: "Fear not: for, behold, I bring you good tidings of great joy, which shall be to all people. For unto you is born this day in the city of David a Saviour, which is Christ the Lord. And this shall be a sign unto you; Ye shall find the babe wrapped in swaddling clothes, lying in a manger." Then a multitude of angels will appear and sing, "Glory to God in the highest, and on earth peace, good will toward men."

It happens as Mr. Jones knew it would, and he can look on with an air of detachment. When the shepherds rise to go to Bethlehem to investigate, Mr. Jones, of course, decides to go along. But despite his effort to keep up with them he falls somewhat behind.

As the shepherds pass into the city a Stranger steps forward and forbids Mr. Jones to come farther. Mr. Jones is angry, very angry. He is not accustomed to being thwarted in this fashion. He demands to know who his adversary is and why he is being detained.

"I am a messenger from God," answers the Stranger, "and you must go no farther."

"But I refuse to be stopped," angrily announces Mr. Jones, who is not used to taking orders. "I must follow the shepherds."

"But do you know where the shepherds are going?" asks the Stranger.

"Of course," replies Mr. Jones loftily; "I know the whole incident. They are going to the stable by the inn to see the Christ Child. I know all about it."

"But why do *you* want to go?" persists the Stranger. "What does it mean to you?"

"I don't know why I need to explain these matters to you," says Mr. Jones indignantly. "I take it that it is my own affair, and you need not assume that it is your business to hinder me."

"Just a moment," returns the Stranger. "There are things you apparently don't understand. That announcement in the fields did not come to you. It came to the shepherds. You are familiar with the external account of the Saviour's birth but you do not comprehend its inner meaning. It is idle curiosity that takes you to Bethlehem, and these things are for the pure in heart, for the humble, for men like these simple but strong shepherds who through their care of the sheep have learned of God, and who through their childlike trust in Him have learned the secrets you have missed.

"You are a proud man, Mr. Jones, proud and self-confident. You are not willing to acknowledge a mistake or a wrong because it would wound your selfish vanity. You boast that you are in debt to no one, when you are in debt to everyone—to the God who gave you life; to your associates and employees, without whom you could not carry on; to your customers, without whose favor you could not continue in business; to the members of your family, who make possible the home you take for granted. Pride has eaten into your spirit, Mr. Jones, and you are not worthy to go with the shepherds."

"But," protests Mr. Jones, who is now on the defensive, "I am not a bad man. I am law-abiding. I am a good provider for my family. I am honest and upright and moral. No scandal has ever smirched my name."

"Mr. Jones," answers the Stranger sternly, "respectability is not enough. Your pride provokes you and multitudes like you to think that you can earn the favor of the Almighty simply by being decent and honest. You cannot receive your salvation until you are willing to confess your unworthiness and accept the forgiveness of God as a gift of His grace which no man can earn for himself. Your sinful pride is your ruin."

All that Mr. Jones can do is to mutter under his breath, "Most irregular, I must say."

As he is about to move away he sees the shepherds returning with a great joy reflected on their faces. The Stranger bows, as if in worship. It suddenly comes to Mr. Jones that the Stranger, despite his conventional attire, is an Angel from God.

It is only a little later that Mrs. Jones flutters up to the doctor in the hospital in visible agitation.

"Oh, Doctor," she says, "the strangest thing has happened. Mr. Jones opened his eyes a moment ago, and I was expecting him to raise a great fuss about being in the hospital and being laid up at a time when he is so terribly busy at the office. But he didn't seem to take it in that he was in the hospital. He just looked at me and asked in a voice that was almost tender, 'Mary, am I a proud man?' That's exactly what he said."

"Was that all?" asks the doctor.

"Yes, that's every bit of it, and then he closed his eyes again and seemed to fall asleep."

"Very strange," comments the doctor. "Very strange, indeed."

III

But Mr. Jones is off on another journey across the centuries and across the miles, so let us observe this next excursion of his mind.

This time, oddly enough, Mr. Jones finds himself riding a camel. He looks about him and discovers that he is in the company of men whom he readily recognizes as the Magi from the East, on their way to Jerusalem. Mr. Jones is riding somewhat behind the others and is surprised to find that one of the men is Matthews, his assistant manager. It is all very perplexing. But again Mr. Jones looks on with a detached air, knowing precisely what is going to be told them when they interview Herod. He recalls that they will go on from Jerusalem to Bethlehem.

As they approach Bethlehem, however, Mr. Jones notices a familiar figure—it's the Angel again. Mr. Jones pretends to be engaged with his camel's trappings when they come near, and affects not to see the Angel. But the Angel has discovered Mr. Jones. Once more he bars the way for Mr. Jones as the others pass on. He compels Mr. Jones to alight.

Mr. Jones is not so brusque this time, but he makes no effort to conceal his annoyance at the delay.

"Can you not see," he says to the Angel, "that my companions are about to leave me? I beg of you not to detain me."

"But why do you want to go with them?" queries the Angel.

Mr. Jones is about to reply as before that it is his own business, but he decides that politeness is the better policy. Before he can answer, however, the Angel speaks again.

"They are going to visit the Christ Child to offer gifts. Have you anything to give if I should let you go?"

"Oh," answers Mr. Jones, with a feeling of relief, "I have made many contributions in His name. I shall be glad to tell Him of my gifts."

"Well, Mr. Jones," says the Angel, "suppose we look at the record."

He grows thoughtful for a moment and then speaks.

"Do you consider yourself a generous giver, Mr. Jones?"

"Oh, indeed, yes," is the reply. "I pledge to my church, and I pay faithfully."

"Yes," answers the Angel, "you contributed a dollar a week to the church last year, and other miscellaneous gifts would bring the total to approximately seventy-five dollars."

Mr. Jones smiles—he is pleased that this unknown Angel should be aware of his benefactions. But he observes that the Angel gives no sign of being impressed.

Mr. Jones is about to move on when the Angel stops him. "Just a moment, Mr. Jones, we have not finished." Then he asks, abruptly, "You smoke, do you not, Mr. Jones?"

"Yes," replies Mr. Jones, who is becoming irritated again. "Is there anything wrong with that?"

The question is ignored as the Angel asks another. "What do you spend for cigars?"

"I suppose about eighty-five cents a day," answers Mr. Jones, not seeing that this has anything to do with his getting into Bethlehem.

"That would be something over three hundred dollars a year," calculates the Angel, "which would suggest that you care considerably more for this form of pleasure than you do for the work of the Master."

Mr. Jones does not like the turn the conversation is taking, so he makes another approach.

"Look," he says, "if I'm not very much mistaken, one of those men going into the town is Matthews, my assistant manager. Surely if he can get in, I can. I'm president of the company, and he is only assistant manager."

The Angel forces a smile.

"Mr. Jones," he replies, "you are a very trying case. Mr. Matthews has a gift for the Christ Child, but you have not shown yet that you have any gifts to offer. Since the language of money seems to be the language you most readily understand, I must tell you that your gifts, in spite of your larger income, do not begin to compare with those of Mr. Matthews."

"Oh," smiles Mr. Jones, missing the point entirely, "that is a matter easily remedied. I'll contribute as much as Matthews does. Now will you let me go?"

By this time the Angel is growing very tired of trying to make Mr. Jones understand.

"Mr. Jones," he goes on wearily, "it isn't a matter of money. It's a matter of the heart. The gift of money is only an outward sign, and not always a good one at that, of the inner disposition of the heart. You give grudgingly as a matter of duty; you were willing to give more just now because you thought by doing so you could buy a favor. Mr. Matthews gives generously because he *loves*. Until you love, your gifts are unworthy. These men who have come with their gifts are bringing the Christ something much greater than material treasure alone. They are bringing the devotion of their hearts. You are not prepared to make so costly an offering, and that is why you must turn back."

So once again Mr. Jones turns sadly away.

And once again Mrs. Jones flutters up to the doctor in the hospital in visible agitation.

"Oh, Doctor," she exclaims, "the strangest thing has happened. Mr. Jones opened his eyes a moment ago and looked straight at me. And what do you think he said? He said, 'Mary, it is a matter of the heart.'"

"But," continues Mrs. Jones, "it can't be his heart, for you told me yourself that his heart is in perfect condition."

"So it is," replies the doctor. "I can't imagine what he meant. It is most peculiar."

IV

The following day Mr. Jones is sufficiently improved to sit up in his room. Mrs. Jones wonders at his manner, though she is afraid to call attention to the change she observes. Mr. Jones has no complaints to make, as she had thought he would, but seems to be preoccupied. Instead of being his usual blustery self he is quiet and thoughtful. At length he turns to his wife and makes a request.

"Send for Matthews, dear, will you, please?"

Yes, he actually says "please," but Mrs. Jones decides to make no comment and hastens to carry out his request.

When Mr. Matthews appears, Mr. Jones wastes no time in coming to the point.

"Matthews, I want the truth. What is your honest opinion about the wages I pay my clerks and about the salaries of our office force?"

Mr. Matthews, having been asked for his candid opinion, proceeds to give it.

"Mr. Jones, to be perfectly frank, the wages and salaries are inadequate. Indeed, if I may say so, they are *grossly* inadequate."

Mr. Matthews flushes when he realizes how forthright he has been, but he is glad that the words are out.

"That is exactly what I expected you to say, Matthews," responds Mr. Jones. "And I am obliged to agree with you. But I am resolved to mend matters. I want you to make a careful study of wage and salary scales and report to me what you think would be not only a fair but a generous schedule for services for the members of our organization. When I have confirmed your estimate we will arrange for the new scale of pay to go into effect the first of the year.

"Meanwhile I want you to plan for a bonus to be given to all our employees. This matter I leave entirely in your hands. Do what you would do if you were in my place. I leave the matter solely in your charge."

Mr. Matthews can hardly believe what his ears are telling him, but Mr. Jones is not through yet.

"And one other thing," continues Mr. Jones. "You are an active churchman, and while I am a member and a regular contributor I must confess I could afford to be more generous in my support of the church's work. I would like for you to think the matter over and later advise me where you think I might best make a rather substantial contribution. But there must be this understanding—no one is to know the source of the contribution. I want to make up for some of my past negligence, and I want to make sure I do it without any stir about it. I hope to improve my habits in the matter of church loyalty and religious interest, and this will perhaps be as good a way as any to begin. But you understand, Matthews, that this is strictly between us."

Miss Brown, Mr. Jones's secretary, is next summoned to the hospital to take some dictation. Seating herself, she waits for the usual fireworks. But Mr. Jones, for some reason, seems not to be in a combustible mood. Miss Brown relaxes a little.

"Address this letter," Mr. Jones is saying, "to my employees and associates in Paramount Department Store."

Miss Brown is thinking to herself, "He should be saying, 'To my underpaid and unwilling slaves'!"

Mr. Jones proceeds with the letter.

"I have just had a conference with Mr. Matthews, my assistant manager, and have instructed him to prepare a new scale of salaries and wages for all our employees which will be appreciably above that now in operation. This new schedule will be put into effect the first of the year and continue on a permanent basis.

"Meanwhile, I have also instructed Mr. Matthews to arrange for each employee a suitable bonus in appreciation of

the services which have made possible the successful operation of the store for the year.

"Let me also announce that henceforth it shall be the
policy of this store to extend to every customer every possible courtesy and kindness. I am asking that this practice
be established not primarily because it may build good will
for the store but because I have come to realize that kindness and understanding are essential to human welfare.
Sincerely yours."

Miss Brown looks up for a moment with a puzzled expression
that is gradually replaced by a smile as Mr. Jones dictates the
next letter.

"Miss Ruth Brown, Secretary to the President, Paramount
Department Store, City," begins Mr. Jones.

"My dear Miss Brown," he goes on. "Permit me to confess
that I have been a very difficult person to work for. I must
also add that in spite of my unpleasant disposition you
have rendered excellent service. What you must have thought
about me I can only imagine. But I am writing now to say
that an old man has realized at least some of his mistakes
and proposes to do better. I trust that you will continue in
our service, and wish to assure you that henceforth you will
receive from the president of the company the same courtesy and consideration which he is asking his employees to
show toward the store's customers. Very sincerely."

When the dictation has been completed Miss Brown finds herself doing what she has never in the wildest flights of fancy
imagined she would ever do—she steps up to Mr. Jones and
plants a kiss squarely on his cheek while Mrs. Jones looks on
with approval and Mr. Jones blushes profusely. Then Miss
Brown quickly makes her exit.

Mr. Jones seems suddenly weary and shortly falls asleep.
When he has closed his eyes, Mrs. Jones tiptoes out of the room

and hunts up the doctor. This time, however, though puzzled, she is quite composed.

"Doctor," she queries, "do you know what Mr. Jones just said? As he dropped off to sleep just now he looked at me and said, 'Mary, I am going back to Bethlehem.'"

"Very odd," the doctor murmurs, "very odd."

V

Of course, it isn't odd at all.

This time as Mr. Jones makes his way to Bethlehem he steps with the stride of one who is confident of his destination, and there is gladness in his countenance.

Again the Angel is at the gate. But as he sees Mr. Jones approaching, he bows in greeting and says, "Merry Christmas, Mr. Jones. And welcome to Bethlehem. You will find the One you seek just ahead."

As Mr. Jones acknowledges the greeting and passes on, he fancies that he observes the Angel wink, and he goes into the city reflecting that perhaps even Angels have a sense of humor.

When Mr. Jones is at the place where the Holy Child lies, he kneels just at the entrance. There he bows and prays. As he looks up he sees the Child smile, and he is sure in his heart that his offering has been accepted.

Mr. Jones is Everyman. Every man must combat the pride that Mr. Jones discovered in his own heart. It may be found in varying degrees and be expressed in an amazing variety of ways, but it is there. And only humble hearts can understand the greatness of the gift God gave in Christ. And only penitent and dedicated hearts may offer in return the treasures that the Holy Child can smile upon.

May God help every man to find his way to Bethlehem and, upon finding the way, to be granted entrance into the city!

Never in Jerusalem

by Pauline Palmer Meek

The stage was set. With a full half hour to wait before Gordon's arrival, the apartment looked perfect. The door to the bedroom was properly closed. The living room desk had the look of an heirloom, although Julie had bought it at a second-hand store. The maple table was centered with a basket of cookies, hardly yet cool, whose spicy smell gave the room a holiday atmosphere. Julie was glad now that she had decided not to decorate a Christmas tree, but had chosen instead the one huge candle to glow softly beside the figurine of a Madonna cradling the Child in her arms. The figurine had not been as expensive as it looked.

She turned to the mirror for a final check of her appearance. The image was exactly what she intended. She looked poised, cool, smooth, the sort of person who had been born to teach French in one of the city's best high schools. The red roses and holly in Gordon's corsage looked elegant against her simple white faille. It was an appropriate costume for attending the Christmas Eve church service and then, no doubt, eating in one of the quiet places Gordon would choose.

The doorbell sounded. How could that be? Gordon had never yet been a half hour early!

A pale girlish face confronted her when she opened the door. "Wow," a husky voice said.

"Rosalie," Julie said flatly, unbelieving. The two stood gazing at each other.

"Aren't you going to invite me in?" Rosalie asked, grinning.

"Come in," Julie said, stepping aside.

Rosalie dropped a large brown paper bag in the middle of the room and inspected her surroundings. "So this is how the other half lives," she said.

A feeling of panic crept into Julie's numbed muscles. "What are you doing here?" she asked.

"I just thought I'd drop in to keep you from being lonely on Christmas, far from home and loved ones." Rosalie had an impish grin.

Her skirt was much too short and much too tight. Her hair was piled too high. A frayed purple coat hung from her shoulders. Julie went through the motions of putting the coat away. "Where is your new coat?" she asked.

"Oh, yes—my new coat. Thanks for sending it. All seven of us greatly appreciate the box of Christmas presents you sent. It was much the nicest coat I've ever had."

"Where is it?"

"In the hock shop, of course. How else could I get my hands on enough money for bus fare to bring me five hundred miles?" Rosalie helped herself to a handful of cookies from the basket.

"You're hungry," Julie said. "Come to the kitchen and I'll fix a snack." She wondered wildly if she could shut the kitchen door to hide Rosalie from Gordon.

"I've been hungrier," Rosalie said, following. "I had a hamburger at the bus station." But she accepted milk and fruit.

"Is it true you've dropped out of school again?" Julie asked.

Rosalie shrugged. "I'm no good in school. You're the only one in the family that ever had any brains."

"I'm the only one who ever tried to use the brains I do have!"

Julie said hotly. "I got a scholarship, yes—but you have no idea how I had to work for it! You have no idea how I drove myself, holding down a part-time job, taking night classes, studying all hours! You could make something of yourself, too, if you would work like I did!"

Rosalie drank milk, saying nothing.

"Mom's last letter said you were talking about getting married."

"Yeah."

"And what would you live on?"

"Rod makes a dollar and a quarter an hour. So it isn't steady work, but he makes good money when he does work."

"Don't do it, Rosalie! You're only sixteen years old! That's no way out."

"Sometimes I think you're right." There was something touching in the slump of her shoulders.

Julie turned to take the brown paper bag to the bedroom. Rosalie stood in the door.

"You're getting ready to go somewhere?"

"A friend is coming any minute now to take me to church."

"Church, yet! A boy friend?"

"A man, yes."

"Who is he?"

"His name is Gordon Campbell. His father owns the Campbell Paper Mill. Gordon is taking over the management of it."

"I get the picture. He lives in a palace full of liveried footmen. Aren't you afraid of losing your glass slipper at midnight, Cinderella? How soon do you expect this handsome prince to propose?"

Julie said nothing, but she knew the burning in her face betrayed her. Sometimes she felt that Gordon was very near to speaking of marriage. Then sometimes he seemed reserved, aloof, as if he felt some lack in her. She had hoped that by spending the holidays here in the city—. Rosalie seemed to read her thoughts.

"All right," Rosalie said. "Pardon me for living. I'm sorry I came. I don't know why I ever imagined you'd be glad to see me. It was the coat, I guess. Nobody ever gave me a brand-new coat before. I should have known you only sent that box because you darn well didn't want to see any part of your family. Show me where you put my things. I'll get out of here in the morning."

"Of course you won't leave in the morning!" Julie protested. She even suggested, too profusely, that Rosalie brush up a bit to meet Gordon.

"You're kidding," Rosalie said coldly. She shut the bedroom door between them.

Rosalie had made herself invisible, but Julie did not risk inviting Gordon in to sample the cookies. The drive to the church was accomplished almost in silence, for Julie was too disturbed to make small talk and Gordon seemed equally quiet. It was a relief to reach the church, where the clangor of chimes filled the air with joyous sound.

Julie gave herself to the service, glad to escape her guilty thoughts. O come, Emmanuel. How silently the wondrous gift is given. No crib for a bed. Myrrh is mine, bitter perfume. Love came down at Christmas, love for plea and gift and sign.

Afterward they sat in a dim little coffeehouse. "Have you heard from your parents?" Julie asked, making conversation.

"Oh, yes. Mother wrote the usual chatter about the round of holiday parties. Dad sent the usual instructions about what should be done at the plant while he is gone. The same instructions he gave me before he left, of course."

"I hope they have a pleasant vacation."

"I doubt if they can, now. I'll have to phone them tomorrow. My sister was taken to a hospital today."

"Carolyn? But I thought you said she and the baby were fine. Is it something serious?"

"I'm afraid so." He did not pursue the topic, but gave attention to his pastry. Then, "You seemed thoughtful at church tonight. What did it mean to you, Julie? What does Christmas mean to you?"

Julie felt her way, hunting for words that would sound right. "The minister's point, of course, was that Christmas is the basic truth about life. Christmas demonstrates that the real meaning of life comes to us in unexpected, improbable ways."

"Like the Son of God in the manger, you mean."

"Yes. And that part about the Wise Men—he meant, I think, that life's meaning is never found in Jerusalem, in the places of wealth or power or learning."

"Where is meaning found, then, Julie?"

"Why, in the unexpected Bethlehems, where people yearn and struggle and recognize how weak they are. Wherever people love each other enough to involve themselves voluntarily in suffering. If God loves us that much, then—." Julie's voice trailed off. She kept seeing Rosalie's wan face in the doorway.

Gordon broke the pause abruptly. "The hospital my sister went to today is a mental hospital."

Julie studied his face, perplexed. "I don't understand. All you've ever told me about Carolyn is that she has a wonderful husband and a beautiful home and, a few months ago, a fine healthy baby."

"I didn't think you would want to be bothered about the real situation. Carolyn was always a moody kid. We thought marriage would make her happy. Then we thought the baby would give her something to live for. But she hardly will look at the baby. She has refused even to speak to her husband for weeks. Yesterday she very nearly succeeded in committing suicide."

"Is there anything I can do? The baby—"

"Bless you! No, the baby has good care. There's nothing you can do. Unless you might go with me some day to call on her."

"Of course. I just can't understand it."

"I was afraid you couldn't. You are such a vital person, so sure of what you want, so interested in living. You really can't understand how life could seem a useless, meaningless burden."

Julie sat quiet. "Is life ever a meaningless burden for you, Gordon?"

"I'm almost afraid to admit it to you. When I first started attending the night class where I met you, it was because our family doctor advised me to broaden my interests. I had gone to him to ask for sleeping pills. He told me I did not need to sleep nearly so much as I needed to wake up. He advised me to throw myself into life and find out what it means."

"Have you found out?"

"Only in glimpses. I don't find meaning at the plant. The foreman knows more about it than I do. Dad talks about retiring, but he never really gives me any responsibility. If I ever have a glimmer of what life ought to mean, it usually comes from you. You really believe what you said about Christmas, don't you? That meaning is never in Jerusalem, but only where people love enough to accept suffering voluntarily."

Julie took a deep breath. "Yes, I really believe it. Although I must admit that I've been trying to forget it, lately. Gordon, I'll have to go home now. Do you mind?" Gathering gloves and bag, she stood.

"Go? Now?" He stared up at her in astonishment.

"I didn't tell you that my sister came unexpectedly this evening. I must go back to her. I only wish I could buy a coat first. I hate to bother you, Gordon, but do you suppose you could help me find a shopping center still open?"

"We can try," he said dubiously, rising.

"This is the last thing I'll ask of you."

He sat down again. "Then I won't go."

She looked at him, startled, then answered his grin with a smile of her own. "All right, then. Maybe it won't be the last thing."

"I do think you might explain why you must buy a coat so late on Christmas Eve," he said when they were moving into the traffic.

"It's a long story. I hurt Rosalie pretty badly this evening. Buying another coat won't make up for it. But talking won't make up for it, either. I'll have to do something dramatic enough to convince her that I'm glad she came and that I want her to stay. You see, she had to pawn the other coat I gave her."

"She pawned the other coat?"

"It was the only way to get money for bus fare. And now she says she's leaving in the morning. She knew, of course, that I didn't want you to see her."

"Julie, I don't understand a thing you are saying."

"I've never told you about my family."

"No. Sometimes I've wondered why you avoid the subject."

"I've avoided it because you certainly would not want to get mixed up with them. I have six younger brothers and sisters. My father walked out on us years ago. My mother does what she can, but my teen-age brothers are completely out of hand. Now Rosalie has dropped out of school too, and threatens to get married. But Rosalie has so much potential! I suppose she came out here in desperation, really. And I shut her out!"

"I can see your problem."

"It wasn't only that I didn't want you to meet her. It occurred to me that I ought to take her in—but how horrified my landlady would be at Rosalie's loud manners and wild clothes. It occurred to me to enroll her in school here—but how shocked my principal would be to know she is my sister. Rosalie knew how I felt about her coming!"

"I see. So you think a coat might help. Well, we've found a shopping center open, anyway."

The plaza was vibrating with Christmas lights and Christmas tunes. In the gaity of festival atmosphere, Julie could almost believe that the coat she found might work magic.

Gordon made a purchase also. "A Santa Claus mask," he explained, eyes dancing. "If you want a dramatic way to convince Rosalie that she is wanted, we might as well give her the whole bit!"

They tiptoed into the apartment like conspirators, giggling over the incongruous effect of Gordon in the mask, the whiskers snowy against his dark suit. Julie went to waken Rosalie.

She smoothed the tousled hair. "Wake up, Rosie. Merry Christmas, honey! Come see what Santa brought!" She pulled the girl to her feet, tied a robe around her, led her to the door.

"Ho, ho, ho," said Gordon from under the mask.

Rosalie examined him soberly. "I never did believe in Santa Claus," she said. "But I know who you are. I'll tell you one thing, though—if you've come to try the glass slipper on me, it won't fit. Glass slippers never fit me."

"What are you talking about? Does this look like a shoebox?" He tossed the coat box to her and pulled off the mask.

"Gordon," she said, grinning back at him. "Gordon Campbell, right?"

"Right," he said, taking her hand in both of his. "Rosalie. You look a little like Julie, don't you?"

"Do I? Nobody ever told me that before."

"Are you going to open the box? Julie didn't hunt all over town for a shopping center just so you could admire the wrapping."

She sat down with the bulky box. Gordon accepted cookies from Julie's basket.

"I don't get it," Rosalie said, staring at the folded coat.

"It's the kind of coat the girls wear here. I want you to stay and go to school with me," Julie said.

"Nobody said anything about my staying."

"I'm saying it now. I want you to stay."

"I can't stay. I didn't bring my clothes . . . anything."

"We'll go back home together and get whatever you need."

Gordon broke in. "In fact, I'll drive you. Shall we go Christmas Day, or wait until the weekend?"

"Oh, no," Julie protested. "I can't ask you to do that!"

"I know. That's why I'm volunteering." He searched her eyes. "It's time your mother meets me, Julie. I want to know your family."

Julie felt her face crumbling. Her careful poise, her pride of achievement, her lonely years of driving effort—all of it seemed to be dissolving into tears.

Gordon fumbled for his handkerchief. He made awkward gestures toward applying it.

"So who needs me?" Rosalie muttered.

No one answered her. No one appeared to notice how carefully she gathered up the coat and its wrappings. No one noticed how quietly she closed the door once more behind herself.

In Search of Christmas

by James E. Fogartie

Cliff Craig propped an elbow on his ancient typewriter, dropped his chin into the cup of his hand, and stared out across the deserted City Room.

For nineteen years he had coaxed news stories out of his machine. Some had fairly jumped from flying fingers, almost as fast as he could cover the long sheets of rough newsprint. Others had come harder, after mounds of paper had whipped out of the roller. Many had won him prizes and awards. But this was the toughest of all.

How simple it had seemed when his managing editor handed him the assignment, with an open expense account and all the time he needed. "Write a *new* Christmas story," Maxwell had said. That was all.

Now the deadline was just one day away—and there was nothing easy about it any more. His mind went back over his straining and searching for the elusive "angle" to make this a really new Christmas story.

He had set out to write a story that would leave out the old stuff—the Star, the Manger, the Inn, the Shepherds, and the Wise Men. All of these were good, understand, but worn thin by much writing and repeated telling. This was going to be completely new, something no one had yet uncovered.

He had gone through his files on Christmas and had reread many of his own stories, but none gave him a fresh cue. He had taken down an anthology of Christmas stories from his bookshelf and read the work of many an author; but still he could find nothing. He knew well the familiar accounts from the Gospels of Matthew and Luke, but after all, everybody knew them. This must be new, thoroughly new.

He found stories about the decree of Caesar Augustus, making comparisons between the Emperor and the Child.

Many efforts seemed to have exhausted the difficult journey of Mary and Joseph to Bethlehem—and the bright Star that shone over the City of David.

He lost count of stories about the Inn with no room, of the Stable, bleak and bare, and of the simple, rough-hewn Manger. Some had portrayed the Innkeeper as a good and godly man, who, with no room in his inn, had done the best he could for Mary and Joseph. At least he had furnished them shelter, a place away from the night air. Others had pictured the Inn-keeper as a hardhearted businessman, concerned only with material gain, caring nothing for those for whom he had no room. The stable had merely been his way of ridding himself of the nuisance of a poor couple for whom he had no concern. These stories were all right; but he must have a new story, a fresh approach.

How many openings the Shepherds had provided! Tales had been told of the littlest shepherd, the oldest shepherd, the skeptical shepherd. Some had built their stories around the young son or daughter of one of the men who spent that night on the Judean hillside. Shepherds were fine, but there was a limit to that angle, too.

Why, stories had even been written around the friendly beasts of the stable, but only so much could be written about animals.

He had given serious consideration to this business of the Wise Men. Certainly there was an air of mystery about them, and that should spur creative writing. He murmured aloud, "Strange old boys, those Wise Men from the East." Looking through his material he discovered Halford Luccock's column clipped from *The Christian Century*. It pictured these men of mystery as Wise Men from the West.

They could be dressed up a bit with Western garb. That would mean, of course, changing their gifts from gold, frankincense, and myrrh to more modern presents. After all, nobody knew anything about those ancient treasures, and cared less. Wise Men from the West. Everything would be changed.

As tradition had it, there were three Wise Men. The first was known as Kaspar. In our day he would be an industrialist, president of the Kaspar Manufacturing Company, Incorporated. His journey would take him out after bigger and better sales. He followed the Star, of course, but his primary concern was for new export outlets. He would get a lot of orders, but such a man would undoubtedly get so wrapped up in his own affairs that he would lose trace of the Star, and, in the end, never reach Bethlehem at all.

The second Wise Man is said to have been Balthazar. He was a Nubian prince, with skin of dark hue. Craig thought of him as an expert in military defense. He would recruit a great army before getting started to Bethlehem, for he might need protection on his journey. So he would spend most of his time in gathering recruits and in solving the problems of logistics. Rome, skeptical of such a force, would of course refuse to allow this army to pass through any of her provinces; thus, Balthazar would never get to Bethlehem either.

As for the third Wise Man, he was usually called Melchior. He, too, sought to find the King; but there were other important things on his mind. As president of Melchior, Melchior and Melchior, Advertising and Public Relations Consultants, he saw the possibility of a big promotion campaign, handled properly. He became busy giving out press releases in every hamlet and town through which he passed. That, along with entertaining local journalists, took time. To complete his coverage he made a detour into Egypt which took several months. By the time he arrived in Bethlehem, the infant King was gone. Melchior never saw Him, nor was he able to present his gift.

Craig mused over this possibility. It was different, yes, but perhaps too bitingly true to life. It was just as well, then, that the Wise Men came from the East. Leave the story that way.

Another clipping told of the efforts of a television star in trying to find a green Christmas tree. In New York City there were plenty of evergreens, but they were not green. All of them had been changed in order to improve their looks. There were silver trees, blue trees, pink trees. Some were even green, but not the natural green of the forest.

Could it be that we have tried to repaint Christmas in our own colors, attempting thereby to make it another novelty? And, in so doing, have we betrayed the shallowness of our own Christian understanding? Of course, this theme could be overplayed and might be misunderstood. Perhaps it would be better to leave it alone.

Pursuing still another idea to its fruitless end, he remembered the question asked in Jerusalem by those mysterious visitors from the East: "Where is he that is born King of the Jews? for we have seen his star in the east, and are come to worship him."

Perhaps the answer to that question would show him the new lead he sought. "Where is he that is born King of the Jews?" It was a haunting question, indeed. It disturbed him, prodded him up from his desk. He left the City Room partly to escape the question, or was it to find an answer to it? He did not know. But he did know that time was running out and that he must quickly find a new Christmas story.

Just outside the building he noticed several men, standing on the curb around a kettle hung from a tripod. With noisily ringing bells they called to passersby for contributions to the needy. "Well," he said, "they are still at it—the same old thing, year in and year out." There was nothing new here.

He passed on down the street. Craig's roving eyes caught the beautifully decorated windows of a large department store.

He decided to go in and look around—why, he wasn't certain. Surely there could be nothing here to give him an idea. He took his time, browsing here and there.

As he had expected there were crowds of people—weary, harried people, all hurrying to make last-minute purchases, wanting speedy service from overworked clerks. He was surprised to note that the clerks seemed cheerful despite their tired faces. "Merry Christmas," they called to departing customers. And the customers, though pushed and jostled and squeezed, managed to smile and say, "Thank you." "Well," he thought, "it seems as though the spirit of the King is here, even among these bustling, shoving crowds."

Out on the street again, he wandered toward one of the big fire stations. He knew the boys there—had covered some fires they had fought. The place seemed unusually busy, more like a toy shop than a fire station. And it was! He had forgotten. These men devoted many hours to repairing and repainting toys for youngsters who would otherwise have a toyless Christmas. Busy men they were, calling happily to one another as they worked. They greeted him enthusiastically, proudly exhibiting their handiwork. As he left, those words of the Master came to him, "Inasmuch as ye have done it unto one of the least of these . . . ye have done it unto me."

Suddenly he stopped, recalling an incident in his own home a few days before. His little daughter had been getting together some gifts for a basket which her Sunday school class was preparing to give to a family who needed help. She had come down from her room bearing one of her favorite dolls and announced she was going to put it in among the gifts. It was in excellent condition, having had wonderful care from its little mistress. With the doll she brought changes of clothing and miniature luggage. Here was a gift to thrill the heart of any little girl on Christmas morning.

He had almost chided her about giving away so fine a possession, but she had said gaily, "Daddy, I want to give this. I've had so much fun with this doll, I want someone else to have fun with her, too. That's what Christmas is all about, isn't it,

Daddy?" Remembering her unselfishness and joy, he recalled some words from C. S. Lewis' autobiography, in which he said that joy can be a means of bringing us to God. "Indeed," he thought, "my little girl seems to know better than I what Christmas is all about. I believe she knows where the King can be found. But that's not getting my story."

On he walked, passing a group of young people happily chatting about the caroling planned for that evening. "Oh, yes, we must go there," said one. "They always seem to appreciate our coming." And another broke in, "But we must not leave out the family down the street. They say it would not be Christmas without carols sung outside the door."

His path led to a great church. He paused to glance in the open door and watched a group busily decorating the sanctuary. Another group seemed to be in the midst of a rehearsal for a pageant or a play. What joy was in their faces! How happily they worked!

On and on he walked, and the sights that met his eyes were familiar and in keeping with the season. Occasionally he saw things that caused him to question whether they were really a part of Christmas; but for the most part the people he met had joy in their faces and a spring in their step. Certainly they seemed to have the spirit of Christmas.

Gradually he became aware of the question of the Wise Men, "Where is he that is born King of the Jews?" It seemed to be ringing louder in his ears. Could this—all that he had seen—give him his story? Could it be that these folk had found Christmas indeed? There were the men with the bells and the kettle, the smiles on the faces of the weary clerks, the words of gratitude expressed by bustling customers, the firemen in their unselfish work, the generosity of his little daughter, the carolers with their singing, the people in the church—all these had been asking the Wise Men's question.

Then he recalled something else. He remembered that one of his friends had refused to help pay for the big office party. He had said, "I'm not against the idea of a party. But I have decided to give my part this year to CARE to help those who have suffered for their freedom and for their faith."

Yes, there was a difference in these people. As the Wise Men before them, they had made a tremendous discovery. They had found the King, and having found Him, they were not content with mere talk. They were worshiping Him with their gifts and with their lives.

Standing upon that city street, the truth dawned upon him. There was no new Christmas story! There never would be one. There was no reason to strive for novelty. The wondrous story of the Babe of Bethlehem was continuously new.

Cliff Craig walked confidently back to his waiting typewriter. There was no need to hurry. Already the story was taking shape in his mind, as if some unseen hand were tapping it out on a moving tape. This would be the best story he had ever written.

My Son

by Armand L. Currie

I have come to spend Christmas with my Son. He told me
where He might be; that is why I am here. I am sure that He
will come before the night has passed. Just now He is probably
standing beside a bed, building the dream of a joyous Christmas
morning in the mind of a sleeping child. Or I fancy that He may
be knocking at someone's door, hoping to get in and deliver a
message of peace to a troubled soul. Perhaps at this moment He
is doing a bit of spiritual surgery, and is binding up a badly
broken heart. My Son is very busy. He will find the time to get
here, though. He has a way of traveling to the far corners of the
earth to keep company with people whose hearts are humble
and whose lips sing praise.

He does not know that I have planned to meet Him. I came
early to surprise Him. This Christmas will be a happy day for
my Son and me.

Before He arrives, I wish to tell you about my Son. That is, I
call Him my Son, though I am really not His father. Have you
ever heard of a man named Joseph, who lived long ago? Well, I
am he.

I can see that you are too kind to think that I am a garrulous old man if I indulge in some reminiscences. Perhaps you will even forgive me if I use a boastful word or two. When you were singing awhile ago about Bethlehem, and the Christ Child, and Mary, your songs were like wings that took me back across the years.

Mary, the Beautiful, was the light of my life. I had been in love with her for years, and she with me. We planned to be married as soon as I could finish the building of a home. You may well imagine the care with which I toiled. Such love as ours was deserving of the best. The floors were smooth, the walls were straight, the doors swung easily on silent hinges. Mary came often to watch the work, and to sit and count the days that stood like unending distance between us and the wedding day. "If you would only stay at home and do your counting, dear, your carpenter could work much faster," I would say.

"Must I infer that you find more joy in working faster than you do in having me by your side?" she would banter.

One afternoon, however, as she came into the house, I knew that it was not a time to tease. Her face reflected both radiance and fear.

"Joseph, can I trust you to believe me?" she asked.

"Can you trust me to believe you, Mary? What a question! Of course you can, my dear," I replied. But I was hardly prepared for what she was about to say.

"There is to be a child," she whispered.

"Mary!" It was the only word I could find, but the tone of it must have justified her fear.

"O Joseph, not that!" she said. "I am the most blessed of all women. The Child shall be the Son of God."

It was too much for me to understand. I could not keep bewilderment from reflecting itself in everything I did. I tried being silent, but the silence was like ice. I tried to tell Mary of my love, but a note of anguish and pity crept into the words. I tried to ask a question, but it was no use.

That night I lay awake wondering what to think and what not to think . . . what to do and what not to do. I loved her so much that I could not bear the thought of accusing eyes being turned toward her. I was minded to put her away for a while. This, after all, seemed the most sensible thing to do.

Then I must have fallen asleep. In a dream I saw an angel and heard him say, "Joseph, thou son of David, fear not to take unto thee Mary thy wife: for that which is conceived in her is of the Holy Ghost. And she shall bring forth a son, and thou shalt call his name Jesus: for he shall save his people from their sins." The dream caused even greater bewilderment.

As the dawn broke, I made ready and ran hurriedly to Mary's home. I was thankful for the new day; I thought there might be healing in its light. It was an early hour to be calling, but I knew she would be awake. The night must have been a restless one for her, even as it had been for me.

"Mary," I called softly. She was not there. The confusion of the room bore evidence that she had packed in haste and gone away, traveling under the mantle of the darkness. I stood in the door and almost shouted her name. It would have been terrible if I had. My doubt had caused her enough pain already. To have awakened the curiosity of the neighbors would have been too much.

That day I did not work on the new home. In the carpenter shop I labored harder than I had ever thought one could. I tried to wash the throb from my heart with the sweat of toil. Not for a moment did I stop or even look up. There came a knock at the door. It was Simeon, an old friend, a priest. I wanted to throw myself on him and feel his strong arms around me, holding my aching heart against his. But Simeon's manner did not invite such behavior. The strange look on his face said that he did not seem to think it was comfort that I needed.

"Put your tools away, Joseph, and sit beside me here where we can watch the sunset," he said.

For a long moment the old priest gazed westward as if he were seeing beyond the golden sky. Why had he come, I thought. Had he come to speak a word of sympathy or regret or pity? Had he come to condemn Mary? I thought that I would kill him if he had.

At last he spoke: "It is true, Joseph; your Mary is to be the mother of God's Son. I have just come from the home of her cousin, Elisabeth. Mary is there now. She is the blessed woman! And you, you are the blessed man. God has chosen her to be the mother of the Saviour; He has chosen you to be the earthly father of His Son. You are to rear Him and to shape His growth in wisdom and in grace until He becomes, indeed, the world's Divine Redeemer." He looked at me from eyes that were very deep and said, "I give you my blessing, dear friend."

"Where are you going, Joseph?" Simeon shouted with a laugh. Silly question for an old man to ask. He knew; I was going to my Mary!

For three months Mary remained as a guest in the home of her cousin. Need I tell you what I did? Not a peg was left missing in the structure of our home.

Cousin Elisabeth stood at the door and waved a blessing to us as we walked away. Hand in hand we traveled. No longer was there fear in Mary's eyes, nor was there doubt in mine. She had been chosen to bear God's Son; I had been chosen to rear the Saviour of the world. She was the blessed woman; I was the blessed man. As we walked, her heart and mine caught the tune of the Temple hymn, "Bless the Lord, O my soul: and all that is within me, bless his holy name."

"Joseph, in love you built this house for me. When we took it from our dreams and made it real, we did not know that we were building it for God's Son," Mary said.

"And Mary's Son," I added.

"And yours, my blessed," she replied.

Mary was soon asleep. The excitement and strain of the journey had been great. Alone, I sat down to review each hour that had passed and to think of the happiness that had been born of such pain. As I thought thus, the memory of Simeon's face kept returning. His words, "You have my blessing, dear friend," began to repeat themselves over and over. And then . . .

Fear suddenly swept into my soul like a gust of winter wind. For the first time I saw the bigness of the task that was mine. I was to be the father of God's Son. He was to be my care. I was only a carpenter. I knew nothing of the world outside of my own little sphere. I only knew how to work with wood . . . how to make toy wagons for little boys, and wooden dolls for little girls, and yokes for oxen. I could rebuild rickety old beds and benches and tables. That was my trade. How could I be expected to rear and train the Child to become the Saviour of the world? Sheer panic drove me to my knees. "O God," I prayed, "a mistake has been made; I am not worthy to call the Christ my Son."

God seemed not to hear, but Mary heard and I told her of my fear.

"God has made no mistake, Joseph," she said. "Surely you must know that He would not trust the rearing of His Son to careless hands or a wicked heart. You, my husband, are a master craftsman with wood. You take green trees which have been twisted and bent by the storms and out of them hew beams that are straight and strong. You take rough timbers and cause their very roughness to have beauty and luster. You never throw away anything that is good. The neighbors bring broken old tables and benches and beds to your shop and under the touch of your skillful hand they become as new again. You love broken things, you love to make them whole. Beside your bench you have learned the art of creating and restoring. Ah, Joseph, God made no mistake when He chose you to rear and train His Son. What you have learned to do with wood, the Saviour of the world must learn to do with people. You can take Him to school in your shop. The people He shall come to save are like the things you make and remake every day."

People are like wood. That was a new thought. Some are bent and crooked, made so by the fierceness of the winds and storms they endure. Some are coarse, others are fine-grained. Some are hard, others are soft. Some are strong, others are weak. Many are easily broken. But all are good—much too good to be thrown away. They need only to be fashioned by a Master's hand to become what God intended they should be.

The years sped by. Trying desperately to keep my heart from

pounding too loudly, I said as casually as I could one morning, "My Son, would you like to go with me to the carpenter shop today?"

That was the beginning. At first I let Him wander through the shop. He was fascinated by the rows of shining tools. He asked me about each one and I let Him get the feel of them all in His own hands. As He watched me work with blades and chisels He laughed, "My father, you handle the wood as if you loved it and did not wish to hurt it."

"I do love it, my Son, every piece," I replied.

Soon I gave Him a place of His own at the bench. I watched the skill and care of His boyish hands grow. Wood was beginning to have a new meaning to Him. He was beginning to see the possibilities that lay in each piece. He worked as if He were a servant helping each piece to take its proper form and fill its proper place.

In the evening, as we journeyed home together and chanced to pass a filthy beggar, or met someone whose face bore marks of sin, or perhaps another whose sad eyes told of something precious that had been broken within, I made it a habit to say, "They are all like wood, my Son; all they need is a Saviour, like a master craftsman, who can take the tools of love and patience and mercy, and make them strong and straight and whole again."

"Yes," the Boy would muse, "all they need is One who can do for them what they cannot do for themselves."

Each day as He went back to His bench, the work of His hands seemed to reflect more and more those qualities of spirit that the Saviour of the world would have to have.

Other years passed that brought us at last to a memorable day. It came so unexpectedly that we were caught completely off our guard. It was a Sabbath. Dressed in our "Sunday best," as you would say, Mary and I made our way to the synagogue. Being humble folk, we sat within the shadow of the door. Presently He was with us. As usual, the congregation sang the hymn of praise, then repeated the Law, and made a prayer for mercy. It was just as any other Sabbath insofar as our worship was concerned. But when a familiar break came in the ritual my Son quietly turned and kissed His mother. He clasped my hand and whispered, "My father." He made His way toward the altar. Taking the scroll, He read, "The Spirit of the Lord is upon me, because he hath anointed me to preach the gospel to the poor; he hath sent me to heal the brokenhearted, to preach deliverance to the captives, and recovering of sight to the blind, to set at liberty them that are bruised, to preach the acceptable year of the Lord."

He closed the book, and gave it to the minister, and sat down. The eyes of all who were in the synagogue were fastened on Him. And He began to say unto them, "This day is this scripture fulfilled in your ears."

"O dear God, this is the day!" Mary whispered.

Yes, it was the day!

We did not wait to hear what the neighbors would say. Mary and I slipped out into the night. The stars above us seemed to shine with the same splendor that shone from a single star over Bethlehem years before. Mary took hold of my hand. She was trembling. Tears splashed down her face, but beneath them was a smile. I think now that there was a prophecy in both the smile and the tears.

"O dear God," she praised, and pleaded.

Hand in hand we walked home together. She was the mother of God's Son; I had reared the Saviour of the world. She was the blessed woman; I was the blessed man. Our hearts were too full for speech. As in that other day when we traveled home alone, our hearts could only catch tune with the Temple song, "Bless the Lord, O my soul: and all that is within me, bless his holy name."

My Son!